Hands-on Culture of
JAPAN

Kate O'Halloran

J. WESTON
WALCH
PUBLISHER
PORTLAND, MAINE

User's Guide
to
Walch Reproducible Books

As part of our general effort to provide educational materials which are as practical and economical as possible, we have designated this publication a "reproducible book." The designation means that purchase of the book includes purchase of the right to limited reproduction of all pages on which this symbol appears:

Here is the basic Walch policy: We grant to individual purchasers of this book the right to make sufficient copies of reproducible pages for use by all students of a single teacher. This permission is limited to a single teacher, and does not apply to entire schools or school systems, so institutions purchasing the book should pass the permission on to a single teacher. Copying of the book or its parts for resale is prohibited.

Any questions regarding this policy or requests to purchase further reproduction rights should be addressed to:

Permissions Editor
J. Weston Walch, Publisher
321 Valley Street • P. O. Box 658
Portland, Maine 04104-0658

1   2   3   4   5   6   7   8   9   10
ISBN 0-3086-7
Copyright © 1997
J. Weston Walch, Publisher
P.O. Box 658 • Portland, Maine 04104-0658
Printed in the United States of America

Dedication

To Heather, Gabrielle, Aileen, and Aoife, who helped in many ways.

CONTENTS

How to Use This Book . . . . *vii*

Subject Area Correlation . . . . *ix*

A Japanese View of Aesthetics 1

Japan: A Closed Society 4

Geography and Japanese Prints 8

Printing from a Block 11

Sushi: What Do You Mean, It's Not Cooked? 16

Gyotaku: Printing with Fish 20

Ichi, ni, san, yon, go: Counting in Japanese 23

Hon, mai, ken: Counting Things in Japanese 28

Making Paper 32

A Game of Go 35

Mon: Heraldic Crests 39

Katazome: Stencil Dyeing 42

Making a Folded Paper Book 48

Haiku 52

Zen Gardens of Sand and Stone 55

Japanese Writing 58

Nihon-no-Kotowaza: Japanese Proverbs 63

Glossary *67*

Resources *68*

How to Use This Book

This book, like the others in this Hands-on Culture series by J. Weston Walch, Publisher, has been designed to help middle school teachers integrate the study of a particular world culture into the curriculum. Textbooks can teach students about the history and geography of an area, but to gain any real understanding, students must also be exposed to the art and traditions of that society as well.

Hands-on Culture of Japan provides 17 ready-to-use activities to help you do just that. Through the projects in this book, students will be exposed to some common Japanese phrases, to the writing and counting systems used in Japan, to Japanese cuisine, Zen Buddhism, and to the art and literature of Japan.

Throughout this book the focus has been on traditional culture, not the aspects of Japanese culture being developed today. That is because so much of Japan's culture, even today, is based on tradition. Learning about the aspects of Japanese culture examined here will help students understand Japanese culture as a whole. Sources like the Internet are excellent ways for students to learn about aspects of modern Japanese culture like *manga* (comic books).

Of course, many important elements of traditional Japanese culture are not included in this book. The theatrical forms of Noh and Kabuki and the related puppet theater Bunraku could take up a book of their own. Japanese clothing and architecture are distinctive, and would offer students a great deal of scope for investigation. Any of these topics would be excellent research projects in addition to the activities presented here.

Most of the projects in this book work well either as individual or as group activities. When a project requires setting up a work station, as in the papermaking and fish-printing projects, you may find it best to divide the class into groups and set up several work areas. You may also find a group approach helpful for some of the other projects. As students deal with such unfamiliar material as the Japanese writing system, they may find it less intimidating to work together to find solutions.

By their nature, all these projects are interdisciplinary. All are appropriate for a social studies class. Most are appropriate for an art class. Some activities are also appropriate for other subject areas; the correlation chart on page *ix* presents these links. If you are teaching about Japan as part of an interdisciplinary team, each teacher can teach the activities appropriate to his or her domain. All the projects have been structured so that the teacher presenting the material does not need to know either the historical context or the procedure for doing the project. Full background details are provided where needed. You can share some or all of this information with students if you wish, but it is not necessary for student completion of the project. The step-by-step student instructions for the activities should need no further explanation. All activities have been tested with middle and high school students.

To motivate students—and continue the theme of Japanese culture—you may wish to tell them that gift giving is an important feature of that society. Small gifts, often beautifully wrapped in handmade paper, are given on almost any occasion— even when there is no occasion at all. You might incorporate this custom into your classroom with small gifts or candy for the first group to finish the Japanese Writing project correctly, or for the group with the most interesting version of the Japanese proverbs

To help demonstrate the process for each activity, you may find it helpful to keep one or two examples of student work for each activity The next time you present the activity, show the student work as models When dealing with unfamiliar concepts or material, it can help students to see work from their peers and form a general idea about what they might be expected to do

Finally, check out the resources in your community If you are lucky enough to be located near a branch of the Japan America Society, you will have easy access to a number of knowledgeable persons Often, such societies have members who are trained in one or more Japanese arts (such as calligraphy and origami) and who are happy to come into a classroom and demonstrate Japanese exchange students are another resource They can often help teach such arts as origami and flower arranging, or they can talk briefly about Japan and demonstrate the three major writing systems of Japan

I hope that you—and your students—enjoy this book, and that it helps deepen your students' understanding and appreciation of Japan

Note· The Japanese character used to set off the directions on the student pages is the character for the word *sui,* "perform."

Subject Area Correlation

	MATH	SCIENCE	LANGUAGE ARTS	ART	SOCIAL STUDIES
Japanese View of Aesthetics				X	X
Japan: A Closed Society				X	X
Japanese Prints				X	X
Printing from a Block				X	X
Sushi				X	X
Printing with Fish		X		X	X
Counting in Japanese	X				X
Counting Things	X			X	X
Making Paper		X		X	X
A Game of Go	X			X	X
Heraldic Crests				X	X
Stencil Dyeing				X	X
Folding Paper Book	X			X	X
Haiku			X		X
Zen Gardens	X			X	X
Japanese Writing			X	X	X
Proverbs			X	X	X

A Japanese View of Aesthetics

OBJECTIVES

Art

• Students will understand that the same object can be perceived in different ways.

Social Studies

• Students will see that people from different cultures may approach everyday things in different ways.

MATERIALS

A Japanese View of Aesthetics handout
reproductions of some Japanese handcrafts, such as pottery bowls, printed fabric and paper, lacquerwork (or, if available, show some actual objects)
optional: two or three utilitarian objects for students to draw
drawing materials
paper

BACKGROUND

In the traditional Western perspective, "art" is one thing, "life" is another. Art that is considered great is often only admired or understood by a few people. Art objects are usually created only to be beautiful, not to serve any practical purpose. They are often displayed in museums and galleries along with other pieces of art.

In the Western tradition, an artist's work somehow separates the artist from "ordinary" people, and the artist isn't always expected to follow ordinary rules. While potters and metalworkers may make some attractive pieces, their work isn't usually considered art, and they are not seen as artists.

In traditional Western painting, certain criteria were used to decide whether piece of art was good or bad. First, it had to look realistic; a landscape had to make the viewer think the scene actually existed somewhere, a portrait had to look like a real person. Second, a painting had to create the illusion of depth, using techniques like perspective, light and shadow, and different values of color. And finally, a piece had to have balance and a suggestion of permanence, of unchanging value, to be considered great art.

By contrast, art is very much a part of daily life in Japan. The beauty of a cup, a bowl, or a garden is seen as just as important as the beauty of a fine painting or print. Everyday household items were designed to be beautiful, and many artists were also craftspersons, designing and making things for everyday use. According to the Japanese aesthetic, it is important to find the beauty in humble things.

Another important element of the Japanese view of beauty is an emphasis on appearing simple. That doesn't necessarily mean that an object must *be* simple, merely that it must create the impression of effortlessness, almost inevitability. A formal Japanese flower arrangement of a few flowers and a branch can look as if it just happened that way, as if the angle of the stems was caused by their growth. But, in fact, a great deal of work goes into creating this effect. The flower arranger carefully chooses stems and blooms for their shapes. Leaves that might distract from the overall shape are cut away. Then the stems are bent to achieve the desired balance. Like Rikyu's garden (described on page 3), discribed on the student handout, a lot of planning is needed to create the effect of simplicity.

In keeping with this idea of simplicity, the traditional Japanese aesthetic emphasizes one visual focus. Unlike the rooms in a beautiful Western home, Japanese rooms are not filled with paintings and sculptures. One piece of art, one flower arrangement, will be displayed in a room to be admired. As the seasons change, so will the art. In spring the flowers will be cherry blossoms, in autumn perhaps a graceful chrysanthemum. From a Japanese perspective, the many objects displayed in a Western home create an atmosphere of confusion, while a Western eye may see a Japanese room as bare and austere.

Although life in Japan has changed dramatically in recent decades, and will continue to change, art in Japan has long been a way of life. The design and order of the home, the utensils used, are often seen in an aesthetic light.

PROCEDURE

1. Distribute the handout. Show students slides or prints of Japanese handcrafts, or display objects, if available. Discuss the different ways in which our culture and that of Japan approach art and aesthetics. Encourage students to look closely at everyday objects. Model by examining some object in the classroom—say, a stool—and trying to see how it can both function well as a stool and be visually attractive.

2. Either direct students to choose and bring in some small, everyday object to draw, or gather a variety of such objects (spoons, ladles, cups, bowls, etc.) in the classroom.

3. Direct students to design their own version of the object in which an attractive appearance is as important as being useful. They should use shading and perspective to create a three-dimensional appearance. Display the finished works with the original objects.

VARIATION

Have students first make a careful drawing of the existing object, then a drawing of their version of the object, and display the two versions together.

ASSESSMENT

Did students attempt to redesign the object to balance form and function? Did students use shading and perspective as directed?

Name _____ Date _____

A Japanese View of Aesthetics

When we look at the art of different cultures, it's important to remember that words like *beautiful* can mean different things for different people. One culture may see an object as beautiful and appropriate. Another culture may see the same thing as strange and ugly. When it comes to art, there is really no right and wrong, good and bad. Sometimes, when you come to understand what an object means, you can start to look at it differently.

In Japan, a story is told about Rikyu, a man who was famous for his beautiful garden. An important lord came to view the garden. The lord walked to the small teahouse at the end of the garden. He was surprised to see no flowers in bloom at all. As he walked into the teahouse, he raised his head. On a stand in front of him, he saw one perfect morning glory. To make this one bloom stand out, Rikyu had cut down all the rest.

Does this story tell you anything about the Japanese tradition of art?

The Western world has its own tradition of art. In this tradition, "art" is an activity very separate from "life." Art objects are usually created only to be beautiful, not to serve any practical purpose. They are often displayed in museums and galleries along with other pieces of art.

By contrast, art is very much a part of daily life in Japan. The beauty of a cup, a bowl, or a garden is considered just as important as the beauty of a fine painting or print. Everyday household items are designed to be beautiful, and many artists are also craftspersons, designing and making things for everyday use. According to the Japanese aesthetic, it is important to find the beauty in humble things.

The Japanese view of beauty also involves things looking simple. That doesn't necessarily mean that an object must *be* simple. In the story about Rikyu, the effect of the one morning glory wasn't really simple. Rikyu had to go to a lot of trouble to achieve it. But it probably seemed almost like an accident that there was only one flower to look at.

Over the next few days, try to look at things around you in a different way. Instead of just labeling things—like "clock," "bowl"—look closely at the shapes of things, at the way they are put together. Some things, like stacking chairs, may seem to have been designed to be as useful as possible, without any attention to how they look.

Choose one common object that you think could be useful as well as beautiful. Design a new version of that object that combines function and beauty. Draw your design, using perspective and shading to make it look realistic.

Japan: A Closed Society

OBJECTIVES

History

• Students will understand some of the consequences of the policy limiting Japan's contact with foreigners.

Geography

• Students will understand some of the role geography played in the history of Japan.

Social Studies

• Students will understand that a society's development is affected by contact with other cultures, or lack of contact.

Art

• Students will understand the ways in which the history of a society affects its artistic development.

MATERIALS

Japan: A Closed Society handout
paper
drawing materials
optional: reproductions of Japanese paintings, prints, and art objects like screens and lacquerwork

BACKGROUND: HISTORY OF JAPAN

The Japanese name for their country—Nihon—means "Origin of the Sun." According to a Japanese myth, Japan was founded when the grandson of the sun goddess came down to earth on a mountain in Kyushu. In 660 B.C. his great-grandson, Jimmu Tenno, founded an empire in Japan. Jimmu Tenno is seen as the first in a line of emperors extending down to the present day, all descended from the sun goddess.

Although tradition says that Jimmu's empire was the first unified Japanese state, historians say it was the Yamato court, early in the fifth century A.D. The Yamato emperors strengthened their position by claiming descent from the sun goddess. At first, they ruled through alliances with other chiefs. As they learned about Chinese statecraft, a system of court ranking was developed.

The Japanese knowledge of China came by way of Korea. The Yamato empire had sent military expeditions to raid Korea, and had set up a Japanese colony there. This contact exposed the Japanese to the advanced civilization of China. Through Korea, Japan learned of China's writing system, Buddhism, the culture of silkworms, and techniques for working with metal.

For several centuries the Japanese borrowed heavily from Chinese culture, but by the ninth century Japan had begun to separate itself from the mainland. As the Japanese adapted what they had learned for their own culture, their new knowledge developed its own distinct character.

Although the emperor was still called the leader of the nation, by this time a family named Fujiwara had actually taken control. Until the eleventh century, the Fujiwaras were the real rulers of Japan. At the same time, a class of warriors, the samurai, was developing. By 1160 a samurai family had become very powerful at court. In 1192 the samurai Minamoto Yoritomo took power and set up a military government, or shogunate. This form of government lasted until 1867.

Although the same kind of government was in power from the twelfth to the mid-ninteenth centuries, it wasn't always very effective. During the Ashikaga shogunate, leaders in the provinces refused to acknowledge the power of the shogun. Beginning with the Onin War of 1467-1477, there was a century of warfare. It was during this period that the first European visitors began to come to Japan, including Dutch and Portuguese traders and Christian missionaries.

The country was unified again between 1560 and 1600. One of the leaders of the unification was Tokugawa Ieyasu. He founded the Tokugawa shogunate in 1600. It lasted until 1867. The Tokugawa shoguns saw that the country needed stability before it could have peace. One of the things they did to achieve stability was to make all Europeans leave the country and to refuse permission for Japanese people to travel abroad. Some Chinese and Dutch merchants were allowed to trade in Nagasaki, but that was the only contact Japan had with other countries from 1639 on.

With no influence from other countries, a flourishing Japanese culture arose. A national market system developed, and artisans created beautiful fabrics, paintings, books, and other works. The distinctive Japanese style was formed.

By the nineteenth century, the Tokugawa government was no longer strong. A merchant class had developed, and the samurai and feudal lords, or daimyo, became less powerful. Peasant uprisings were common. The economy was foundering.

When U.S. Commodore Matthew Perry arrived in Japan in 1854, the shogunate was losing power. Perry insisted that foreign ships should be allowed to come to Japan. Support for the Tokugawa regime collapsed. In 1867 the shogun was forced to retire. In 1868 imperial government was restored under the young Meiji emperor.

Although the country was now open to the West, it was still a secluded, feudal society. A group of farseeing leaders worked to modernize Japan. They sent fact-finding missions around the world to bring back new ideas and technology. Within a few decades, Japan became an industrialized world power.

Adopting the slogan "rich country, strong army," Japan started a program of military expansion. In 1894 Japan fought China and gained control of Korea. In 1904 they fought Russia and added southern Sakhalin to its empire. In 1909 Japan formally annexed Korea. By the time the First World War began, Japan was a major military power and an industrialized nation.

During the early 1930's, the whole world faced economic troubles. Some military leaders argued that military expansion would give Japan new sources of raw materials and new markets to sell its goods in. The Japanese seized control of Manchuria in 1931, renaming it Manchuko. They became allies with Nazi Germany;

in 1941 Japan attacked the U.S. fleet at Pearl Harbor and occupied European colonial possessions in Southeast Asia. Although the Japanese won at first, they were eventually driven back by Allied troops. In August 1945, the United States dropped atomic bombs on Hiroshima and Nagasaki, destroying them completely. Japan soon surrendered to the Allied Powers.

Since then, Japan has again re-created itself. Although there is still an emperor, the government is now a democracy. In rebuilding Japan's ruined industrial base, new technology was used. The economy recovered rapidly. A farsighted trade policy meant that Japanese manufacturers had large shares in foreign markets, while other countries didn't sell much to Japan. Today, Japan continues to export more than it imports. The country is prosperous and stable.

PROCEDURE

1. Distribute the handout. If you wish to give students more details about Japan's history, use the information in the Background section on these pages. If you wish, you may show students reproductions of Japanese art to show the kind of art that developed in Japan during the years of isolation.

2. Decide whether you want to specify more details of what students should include in their drawings. For example, you might ask all students to show one room in a house in their imaginary society, or to show an overview of a city, using one- or two-point perspective. Explain any additional requirements you may have.

3. Have students proceed as directed on the handout.

ASSESSMENT

Did students successfully create a society that showed no influences from an outside culture? If required, did students use the specified perspective to create the illusion of three dimensions? Did appropriate lines converge on their vanishing points? Were all vertical lines parallel? Did students meet any other requirements you specified?

Japan: A Closed Society

A Japanese myth says that Japan began in 660 B.C. when the grandson of the sun goddess came down to earth on a mountain in Kyushu. However, historians date Japan back to the early fifth century A.D.

For several centuries after Japan became a unified country, the Japanese borrowed a lot from China and Korea. They borrowed the Chinese system of writing. They also learned about cultivating silkworms and the teachings of Buddhism from China.

But around the ninth century, Japan stopped looking for new ideas from other countries. The people of Japan began to adapt the ideas they had borrowed until they took on a distinctly Japanese character.

Then, around 1470, the first travelers from Europe came to Japan. Japan again started to receive new ideas from other places. Dutch and Portuguese traders brought European goods to exchange for Japanese things. Christian missionaries tried to convert Japanese people from their own religions to Christianity. For the first time, Japanese artists saw Western paintings, with their different approach to depth and perspective. Many people were interested in these new ideas.

Between 1467 and 1600, much of Japan was involved in warfare. Some leaders refused to obey the government and fought to do things their own way. In 1600 a powerful leader, Tokugawa Ieyasu, unified the country and tried to bring peace. To help make the country more stable, he made all Europeans leave the country. He said that Japanese people couldn't become Christians or use other European ideas. Some Chinese and Dutch merchants were allowed to trade in one city in Japan, but nowhere else. Japanese people weren't allowed to leave the country and travel to other places. If they did leave, they were forbidden to return so that they wouldn't bring back ideas from the outside world.

With no influence from other places, a distinct Japanese culture arose. Artists created beautiful paintings, prints, fabric, and decorative objects. Japanese literature blossomed.

Finally, in 1854, Japan was again opened to the West. The Japanese quickly learned about Western technology and other ideas, and adapted them to their own use. But the unique Japanese culture remained.

遂 Imagine living in a society that has no contact with the rest of the world, where everyone has the same ethnic background and the same culture. What would such a society be like? What would their houses, their towns, their cities look like? What kind of furniture would they build? How would they dress?

Draw a scene showing some aspect of this imaginary society. Include as much detail as you can. Remember, this society can show no influence from any other culture, including the Western world of today. Be consistent!

Geography and Japanese Prints

Teacher Guide Page

This activity is based on one created by Lee A. Makela of the Department of History at Cleveland State University, Cleveland, Ohio. That activity, which includes reproductions of 15 prints by Hiroshige, is available on the World Wide Web at http://www.csuohio edu/history/japan.html, and can be downloaded for use in the classroom.

OBJECTIVES

Social studies

• Students will understand that information about a culture or geographic region is not limited to written sources.

Geography

• Students will be able to use visual resources to identify the physical characteristics of a region.

Art

• Students will understand how environment and culture affect works of art.

Science

• Students will understand that the earth's surface can be shaped by geological events.

MATERIALS

Geography and Japanese Prints handout
transparencies of 15 to 20 landscapes by Hiroshige or Hokusai, or
books or postcards offering full-color reproductions of the prints

PROCEDURE

Note: This activity can be done in class, as homework, or as an extra-credit project. As an outside assignment, students should locate appropriate reproductions themselves; they should also include a listing of the prints they used as part of the project. If you provide the reproductions or transparencies, direct students to skip the step that asks them to locate reproductions, and move on to the next step.

1. Distribute the handout to students. Tell them that, in this activity, they will be using wood-block prints as a way of learning more about Japan's climate and geographic features. If you are using transparencies, point out in the first image some of the features that provide information about the region, such as physical features, houses and other structures, and human figures included in the landscape.

2. Show the rest of the transparencies, allowing students time to find and identify features that give information about climate, geography, and geology. If you wish, ask students to answer the bonus question.

3. Direct students to write their summary paragraphs.

Features students should notice include:

Geographical features
mountains and rocky crags
volcanoes
forests
rich vegetation
rivers, oceans, streams, waterfalls
marshes and swamps

Climate
Temperate, four-season climate, evidenced by prints showing rain, sun, snow, fog

BONUS QUESTION

Japan is extremely prone to earthquakes, registering an average of 20 a day. The post-and-beam construction of traditional Japanese houses makes them more flexible than houses made of stone; they can "give" a little during an earthquake. Also, the modular construction and easily worked materials of the traditional Japanese house make it much easier and quicker to rebuild than a stone house.

EXTENSION ACTIVITIES

• Japanese prints were first seen in the West in the late 1860's—the heyday of the Victorian era, with its overstuffed, fussy interiors. The clean lines and apparent simplicity of Japanese prints, with their sparse interiors, had a considerable effect on Western arts. Artists such as Mary Cassatt, Vincent van Gogh, and Claude Monet began to borrow the flat spaces and clear colors of Japanese prints. Have students examine Western art of the late nineteenth and early twentieth century for traces of Japanese influence, and report on their findings. Ask them to include an explanation of why they think Japanese prints and artifacts had such an effect in the West.

• Have students do the Printing from a Block activity on page 14 as a follow-up to this activity.

ASSESSMENT

Did students successfully identify many of the features listed? Did the written paragraph establish a relationship between the features named and the geography and geology of Japan?

Geography and Japanese Prints

From 1640 to 1854, Japan kept itself isolated from the rest of the world. After contact was made again, many Japanese things were exported to the West. People in Europe and America were charmed by the elegance of Japanese design. Many Western artists began collections of Japanese imports, particularly the lovely wood-block prints.

These prints had been created in Japan since the seventeenth century. Unlike fine-art forms in many other countries, Japanese prints weren't just designed for rich people. They were made to give pleasure to ordinary men and women. With their fine design and superb printing, they still give us pleasure today. However, these prints can do more than just give us pleasure; they can also show us a great deal about the climate and geography of Japan.

Ando Hiroshige and Katasushika Hokusai were two of the greatest Japanese artists of the nineteenth century. Both men designed a number of landscapes, often in sets. Hiroshige's sets included the *Thirty-six Views of Fuji*, *One Hundred Views of Edo*, *Fifty-three Views of the Tokkaido*, and *Views of the Sixty-odd Provinces*. Hokusai's series included *One Hundred Views of Fuji*, *Thirty-six Views of Fuji*, *Novel Views of the Famous Bridges in Various Provinces*, and *Going the Round of the Waterfalls of the Various Provinces*.

For this activity, you will need to find reproductions of 10 prints from one or more of these series. List the names of the prints and of the artist.

Now, examine the prints carefully for information about Japan's climate, geographic features, and geology. List all the features you find that give you this information. Write a short paragraph to summarize your findings.

Bonus question

Most of the houses shown in these prints seem to be made of wood, paper, and straw, although stone for building is easily available. Why do you think this might be?

_____

_____

_____

_____

_____

Printing from a Block

OBJECTIVES

Art

- Students will know and compare the characteristics of artworks in various eras and cultures.
- Students will create a one-color linoleum block print.

Social Studies

- Students will see how a visual arts medium contributes to the development and transmission of culture.

MATERIALS

Printing from a Block handout
tracing paper
carbon paper markers
sheet of linoleum cut to size for individual prints, or precut pieces of
    lino for printing
linoleum-cutting tools
water-based printing inks
tile or glass for rolling ink
brayer
newsprint
newspaper or other material to protect work surface
paper
wooden spoon or other hard, smooth object to rub print
optional: mon design from the Mon: Heraldic Crests activity on
    page 39.

BACKGROUND

Wood-block prints are one of the most commonly seen examples of Japanese art. Reproductions appear in a number of settings and on a variety of modern-day items. Landscape prints are especially popular: Hokusai's *Great Wave* can be seen on everything from T-shirts to television ads.

The creation of a Japanese wood-block print required a team of craftsmen, employed by a publisher. The publisher was the key figure in the system, as he owned both the workshops where the prints were made and the shop where they were sold. The publisher ordered a design from an artist, usually an independent contractor working in his own studio. The artist drew the design in black ink on white paper and delivered it to the publisher. A copyist working for the publisher traced the original design for the engraver. The engraver then pasted the copy facedown on a block of wood. When the paper was partly dry, the back of it was rubbed away with the fingers until the design could be seen. The block was then carved to leave the design—reversed—standing out in relief. This was the key block, the block used to print the black outlines of the design.

To create the blocks for the other colors, the key block was inked and a print made for each color. These prints were used to transfer the design to the blocks in the same way as the key block design. The areas to be printed in each color were left in relief, while the rest of the block was cut away. To make sure that all the blocks matched up accurately on the finished print, two ridges were left on each block. As each block was printed, the paper was aligned with the ridges, and each part of the image printed in the right place.

The artists who created wood-block prints were prolific, and the prints were popular. They were inexpensive enough that anyone could buy them. Popular subjects included prints of actors, prints showing detailed nature scenes, and landscapes. The landscapes were treated almost like postcards today. A person who visited a scenic district would buy a print showing the view. Certain views—like the Tokkaido Road—were particularly popular, and many artists depicted them.

PREPARATION

If you bought the linoleum in sheet form, cut it to size with a paper cutter or large shears. A size of 6" × 9" is good for most student projects.

PROCEDURE

1. Distribute the handout and go over it with students. If students have designed a family or personal crest in the mon activity on page 39, you may wish to have them use that design here, as the mon design should be a one-color design made of simple shapes that are easy to cut. Distribute all the materials except the linoleum-cutting tools.

2. Have students prepare their designs and transfer them to the lino as directed. Remind students that the finished print will show the reverse of the image on the block.

3. Linoleum-cutting tools come in sets with round and V-shaped gouges. The V-shaped gouges are used to cut fine lines, and the round ones are used to cut wide lines and large areas. Before distributing the tools to students, demonstrate the proper way to use them, with the gouge always cutting *away* from the hand that holds the block. Make it clear that cutting toward the supporting hand is likely to result in serious injury. Also, uneven pressure on the gouge can easily cause it to slip and drive the sharp point into the hand. Distribute the tools. Be prepared to remove the tools from any students who cannot keep this rule in mind.

4. Have students proceed as directed on the handout.

VARIATIONS

- There are several other options if you wish to give students the opportunity to do relief printing but do not feel comfortable with lino cutting. The simplest is to use the foam trays on which meat and other produce are sold. Wash the trays thoroughly, then remove the raised edges Students use the flat central area as their printing block. Moderate pressure with a blunt tool will compress the foam, making it possible to achieve a raised and depressed effect. Since the difference between the raised and depressed areas is slight, less pressure is needed in making the print. There are also several commercial products suitable for printmaking avaible through art suppliers.

• Have students work in groups to create a two- or three-color print. To make sure register is correct, use a print from the first block to transfer the design for the other colors.

• If students have done the Making Paper activity on page 34, they can use their handmade paper for printing.

EXTENSION ACTIVITY

The Geography and Japanese Prints activity on page 10 is an excellent introduction to this activity.

ASSESSMENT

Did students successfully transfer a design to a linoleum block, carve away the background, and make a finished print?

Printing from a Block

Many pieces of Japanese art are useful objects that have been made beautiful. Lacquered cabinets, painted screens, and beautifully patterned kimonos are all examples of this. Japanese wood-block prints are not; these prints are made only to be decorative.

Wood-block printing in Japan began around 1660. Early prints only used one color—black. The design was drawn on the block, and everything that was not to be printed was carved away. Sometimes the black-and-white print was then hand-painted for a more colorful effect.

By the middle of the 1700's, colors were being added during the printing process. This meant that a separate block of wood had to be carved for every color. If you wanted to print an image of a purple iris with green leaves by a blue stream, with details outlined in black, you would need to carve four separate blocks.

black key block   purple block   green block   blue block

Then, when you printed them, you would have to make sure every block was in exactly the right place on the print. Otherwise your finished print could come out looking a bit odd.

Making a full-color wood-block print is very difficult. But linoleum printing uses a similar technique, and is much easier. As in making wood-block prints, you draw your design on the surface of the block and cut away everything you don't want to print. In this activity you will make a one-color lino print.

finished print

1. Work out a design for your print. Remember that the areas you cut away don't print, and that the areas you leave do. If you want to print a fine line, you will need to cut away all the lino around the line, but leave the line there. Keeping this in mind as you create your design will make the cutting stage easier.

2. Transfer your design to the lino block using carbon paper. Since lino printing is an offset process, your finished print will be the reverse of the design carved on the block. If you cut a face looking toward the left of your block, the printed

(continued)

Printing from a Block *(continued)*

image will show the face looking toward the right. If you want your finished print to be exactly the same as your original design, you should use this method: First, trace your design onto tracing paper. Put a sheet of carbon paper over the linoleum block. Then turn the tracing paper over so that the drawing faces down, and place it over the carbon paper. Draw over all the lines to transfer them to the lino. Remove the carbon paper and go over all lines with a marker. Your image will now print exactly the same as your design.

3. Using linoleum-cutting tools, cut away the linoleum outside the lines of your design. Leave the areas you have marked alone. When you have finished cutting, your design will appear to be raised above the surface of the block.

4. To print, place the block on a pad of newsprint. Squeeze ink onto the glass or tile rolling surface. Run the brayer back and forth over the ink until the ink is no longer slippery. The texture will seem sticky, and it will make a slight crackling noise as the brayer runs over it.

5. Use the brayer to transfer ink to the block. Run the brayer through the ink on the glass a few times, then run it over the block. Repeat this process until the block is evenly coated with ink.

6. If you have smeared ink on the newspaper under your block, remove the top sheet. The block should be sitting on a clean surface. Do a test print with a sheet of newsprint. Carefully place the paper on top of the block and rub it well. You can rub with the side of your hand, or you can use a wooden spoon or other hard, smooth object. If the print is rubbed well, the design should be visible through the paper.

7. Peel the test print off the block. Was the block evenly inked? Did you cut all areas correctly? You will often find that some areas need to be cut away more to get the effect you want. After correcting the block, do another test print.

8. Once your print appears the way you want it, you are ready to make finished prints Experiment with different papers and ink colors until you have an effect that pleases you.

Sushi: What Do You Mean, It's Not Cooked?

OBJECTIVES

Social Studies

- Students will understand some of the ways in which environment can affect culture.

Art

- Students will demonstrate the ability to arrange homely objects to create a pleasing visual effect.

MATERIALS

Sushi: What Do You Mean, It's Not Cooked? handout

short-grained white rice (not instant rice, converted rice, or brown rice)

sushi vinegar

nori (seaweed) sheets

wasabi (Japanese horseradish); comes in cans of powder. *(Note:* This is *very* hot!)

sliced pickled ginger, available in jars

cucumber—the long European kind is easier to use than the common short kind

soy sauce

wooden spoon

bamboo rolling mat

a sharp knife

optional: avocado, must be perfectly ripe
imitation crab sticks

BACKGROUND

Japan's cuisine is very much the result of its geography. The traditional Japanese diet is based mainly on rice, fish, and vegetables. Rice is grown on terraced hillsides, suitable to the mountainous land. All the products of the sea, from fish to sea urchins to seaweed, are used as food. Japanese chefs have even found a way to eat the *fugu*, or puffer fish. This fish emits a deadly poison, paralyzing its victims and causing death by suffocation in as little as 15 minutes; fugu is considered a rare delicacy and costs over $100 per serving. It can only be prepared by specially trained chefs. Little meat is eaten in Japan, largely because it takes far more land to graze a cow for beef than it takes to grow rice and vegetables.

Since the principal crop grown in Japan is rice, and fish is the main source of protein, dishes that combine rice and fish are common. Sushi, one of the best-known

Japanese foods, is one of them. Westerners often think that *sushi* means raw fish, but this is not the case; the word *sushi* means "vinegared rice," and refers to the way the rice for this dish is prepared. While raw fish is often a component of sushi, it is not an essential part. (On the other hand, sashimi, another Japanese dish, consists only of slices of raw fish.)

As in most other aspects of traditional Japanese life, Japanese cuisine involves the eye as well as the appetite. The careful arrangement of the food, and the artistic choice of the dishes in which it is served, are as essential to enjoyment as the actual preparation of the food. When food is served, an individual serving of each type of food is placed in a separate container. The large serving dish from which all diners are served, and the large dinner plate on which different types of food are mixed, are not part of traditional Japanese tableware.

PREPARATION

This is one activity that you might want to practice once at home before introducing it to students. You may wish to prepare the rice and vinegar mixture ahead of time; wrap it closely in plastic wrap until you are ready to use it. Prepare the wasabi as directed by the manufacturer. Then you only need to do the assembly work in class.

1. Distribute the handout and go through the different steps with students.

2. Distribute the materials and demonstrate the process. Have students proceed as directed on the handout. *Note:* For safety, keep the knife in your possession, and either cut the rolls yourself or supervise the process. Cutting sushi is much easier if you keep the knife wet by wiping it with a damp towel between cuts; otherwise the rice sticks to it and makes cutting difficult. Prepared *wasabi* looks a little like guacamole, but eating more than a tiny amount will cause considerable discomfort. Because wasabi is so strong, you may wish to delete it from this project, in case a student inadvertently consumes more than a very small amount.

VARIATION

To make a California roll instead of a cucumber roll, use avocado, crabmeat, and cucumber. Place a strip of avocado, one slice thick, across the rice. Split a piece of imitation crab leg in half lengthwise and place the two halves on top of the avocado. Add strips of cucumber next to the crab and on top of the avocado. Proceed as for *kappamaki* (cucumber roll).

EXTENSION ACTIVITIES

Choose two or three other simple Japanese dishes, like *miso* soup, and prepare a complete Japanese meal.

ASSESSMENT

Did students prepare a sushi roll and arrange it attractively on a dish with the appropriate accompaniments (ginger, soy sauce, wasabi)?

Sushi: What Do You Mean, It's Not Cooked?

The country of Japan is a crescent-shaped sweep of islands off the eastern coast of Asia. The four largest islands, which make up most of the land area of Japan, are Hokkaido, Honshu, Kyushu, and Shikoku. Formed by undersea volcanoes, the islands are actually the tops of a submerged mountain range.

Very little of the land of Japan can be used to grow food. Most of Japan is very mountainous, so people can only live, build factories, and grow crops on about one fifth of the land. Less than one fiftieth of Japan is suitable for pasturing animals, and only about one eighth can be used to grow crops.

Since the Japanese can't get much food from the land, they have learned to find what they need in the sea. Japanese cooking emphasizes what nature provides. Along with the fish and shellfish commonly used in other parts of the world, Japanese cooks use a variety of seaweeds. They also include sea creatures like the sea urchin in their recipes. They have even developed a way of getting past the deadly poison of the *fugu*, or puffer fish; it is served, by specially trained chefs, as a great delicacy.

Since the principal crop grown in Japan is rice, and fish is the main source of protein, dishes that combine rice and fish are common. Sushi, one of the best-known Japanese foods, is one of them. The word *sushi* means "vinegared rice."

1. Prepare the rice; it should be slightly firmer than you would use for most dishes. Use one cup of rice to one cup of water. You will need about a cup of rice for each sushi roll. Bring the rice and water to a quick boil. Allow it to boil uncovered for one minute, then cover it and reduce the heat. Let the rice simmer for 20 minutes, then remove it from the heat and let it stand for 10 minutes

2. Put the hot rice in a large bowl and sprinkle it with sushi vinegar; you should use about one tablespoon of vinegar for each cup of rice. Mix the vinegar into the rice with quick, cutting strokes. You are trying to cool the rice as quickly as possible while you mix in the vinegar, so try to expose it to the air as much as possible.

3. Spread the bamboo mat out in front of you, and place a piece of plastic wrap over the mat; this will keep bits of rice from getting stuck in the mat. Place a piece of *nori* (seaweed) on top of the plastic wrap.

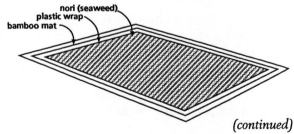

(continued)

4. Spread about a cup of rice on the sheet of nori, leaving about an inch of uncovered nori at the edge farthest from you. The rice is sticky and may be hard to spread. Avoid adding more rice so as to cover the whole sheet of nori; too much rice will make the  sushi hard to roll up, and the finished product will be lumpy looking. The rice should be less than $\frac{1}{4}$" thick. You should be able to see nori through it.

5. To make a kappa (cucumber) roll, peel the cucumber, seed it if necessary, and slice it into strips about one-half inch wide. Lay the cucumber strips end to end across the middle of the rice.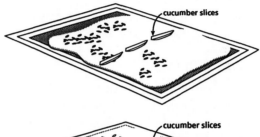

6. Slowly lift and turn over the nearest edge of the bamboo mat and plastic wrap so that the nori folds over on itself and starts to form a roll. You should apply some pressure to keep the roll together, but not too much, or the roll will vary in thickness.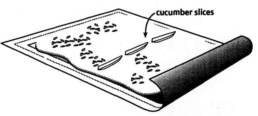

7. Continue rolling until you reach the far edge of the nori—the edge with no rice on it. Moisten the exposed nori with water and press the edge against the roll to seal the edge.

8. Wrap the completed sushi roll in the mat or a napkin and leave it to rest for five minutes.

9. Using a sharp knife, cut the roll in half, then cut each half into thirds or quarters. Lay the rounds flat on a small dish to serve. Garnish with a few slices of pickled ginger and a small knob of prepared *wasabi*.

10. To eat sushi, pour a little soy sauce into a shallow dish. Add a small amount of wasabi—be careful, this horseradish is very, very hot—and mix until smooth. Using chopsticks, dip the sushi into the soy sauce/wasabi mixture and eat. *Itadakimasu!* (Enjoy!)

Gyotaku: Printing with Fish

OBJECTIVES

Art

- Students will successfully make a one-color print from a natural object.
- Students will see that a commonly disregarded object can be used to create something beautiful.

Social Studies

- Students will see that the same resource can be used in different ways by different cultures.

Science

- Students will make careful observations of the surface and structure of a fish and the ways in which it is suited to its environment.

MATERIALS

Gyotaku: Printing with Fish handout
fresh fish with distinct scales, fins, etc. (or rubber fish replica, available from Nasco specifically for gyotaku; see Resources section)
ink and poster paints
soft brush or sponge to apply ink
paper
newsprint

BACKGROUND

Gyotaku, or fish printing, is a wonderful example of the Japanese precept of "finding beauty in the humble." An actual fish is inked and placed on paper or cloth, where it leaves a mirror image of itself, complete with scales, gills, and fins. In black ink on white paper, it is striking; in colored inks or tempera paints, it is intriguingly lovely. No matter how your students choose to do their gyotaku, they will learn how to appreciate the marvelous structure of a fish and to see that beautiful things can be created from unlikely elements.

This technique developed as a way to keep records of fish caught. In Japan, a mountainous land where little can be wasted, the Western approach of taxidermy for a prize catch was not appropriate. Using gyotaku, a fisherman could both record the catch and use it as a meal. Today, gyotaku are sometimes displayed on the walls of homes; sometimes they are kept in a journal to document a successful fishing spot. There are Japanese archives with records of fish caught some 200 years ago. Japanese fishing magazines hold yearly contests for the largest fish caught; judging is done from the gyotaku.

PREPARATION

1. Procure a very fresh fish to use for printing (or purchase a rubber gyotaku fish). An absolutely fresh fish has no odor, the scales are crisp, and the eye is firm and shiny. Anything less fresh can be unpleasant to work with, and as the scales lose definition and peel, the resulting print will be less successful. Choose a fish with an interesting shape and prominent details. It can be easier for students to get a complete impression from flat fish, where the highest point of the fish is not too far from the fins.

2. Use a little alcohol or vinegar to clean any traces of oil or mucus off the surface of the fish. The fish should be clean and dry before printing begins.

3. Set up the work area. To protect the surface, lay down several layers of newsprint.

4. Arrange the fish on top of the paper, spreading out the fins and tail. (As they often tend to fold up against the body, you may want to attach them to the paper with pins.)

PROCEDURE

1. If desired, divide students into groups. Distribute the handout and materials.

2. Students should proceed as described on the student handout.

3. After a few students have taken an impression from the fish, remove the uppermost sheet of newsprint under the fish, as the drips and spills that collect there will show up as smears on successive prints.

Note: The first time students try gyotaku, it may be easiest to use black ink only. Students can experiment with printing black gyotaku on colored paper. In later sessions, or if you have several fish to use at once, different colors can be used.

VARIATIONS

• To make a colored gyotaku, use colored inks or tempera paints thinned to a usable consistency. Use a different color on different parts of the fish—for example, brush yellow paint on the face, pink on the fins and tail, blue on the upper part of the body, green on the lower part. Print as usual. More attention must be paid to cleaning the fish between impressions or the colors will become murky.

• To make a gyotaku fabric print, use fabric printing inks or fabric paints and appropriate fabric. T-shirts printed with gyotaku are very effective.

ASSESSMENT

Did students prepare a completed gyotaku? Was the impression sharp and clear? Were the fins and tail spread out and clearly defined?

Name _____ Date _____

Gyotaku: Printing with Fish

In the West, if you land a prize fish, you can do one of two things: Either preserve a record of the fish by having it mounted, or eat it. You can't do both. The Japanese have found a way of both keeping a record of a prize catch—or even a not-so-prize one—and eating it too. It's called *gyotaku*.

Gyotaku involves making a print directly from a fish. The process transfers all the details of the fish onto paper, giving you a clear record of the fish. You may be surprised at how interesting a fish can be.

Have you ever looked really closely at a fish? Before you start to print, look at the one your teacher has given you. Examine the mouth and eyes. Look at the way the fins open and close. See how the scales fit against each other. Run your hand over the fish's body, first in one direction, then the other. What do you notice? How does the fish's design make it ideally suited to living in water?

When you're ready to begin printing, follow the steps listed here.

1. Take a brush or sponge and completely cover the entire surface of the fish with ink or paint. Pay particular attention to the fins and tail. It's very easy to miss them, and then your printed fish will look strange.

2. Next, lay a piece of soft, thin paper over the fish.

3. With one hand, hold the paper firmly against the middle of the fish. With the other hand, carefully smooth the paper against the fish.

4. Press the paper down so that it comes in contact with every part of the fish. Again, pay particular attention to the fins and tail. Make sure the fins and tail are fully spread out.

5. Finally, starting at one corner, peel the paper slowly away from the fish.

6. Sign and date your finished print.

Step 1

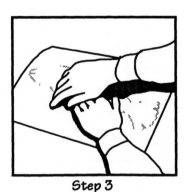

Step 3

 Hands-on Culture of Japan

Ichi, ni, san, yon, go: Counting in Japanese

OBJECTIVES

Math

- Students will see that numbers using a decimal system follow the same rules even if the words used for the numbers are changed.

- Students will see how another culture addresses numeration and will connect it to the system we use.

Social Studies

- Students will compare similarities and differences in the ways two cultures address the same problem.

MATERIALS

Ichi, ni, san, yon, go: Counting in Japanese handout
paper and pencils

PROCEDURE

1. Distribute the handout and go through the information with students. Encourage students to see patterns in the way Japanese number words are formed. The numbers from zero to ten are named. Numbers in the teens are formed by adding the appropriate digit to ten: eleven is *juichi* or ten/one, etc. The numbers twenty, thirty, forty, etc., are formed by combining the appropriate digit with the number ten. Thus twenty is *nijuu*, or two/ten, fifty is *gojuu*, or five/ten, and so on.

   Number words between twenty and thirty, forty and fifty, and so on are formed by adding the appropriate digit to the multiple of ten. Thus seventy-five is *nanajugo*, or seven/ten/five.

   A similar pattern is used for numbers above one hundred. The numbers one hundred, one thousand, and ten thousand have individual names; one hundred thousand is written as ten/ten thousand; one million is one hundred/ten thousand; and ten million is one thousand/ten thousand.

   As students look for these patterns, draw attention to the fact that consonants on some number words change, depending on the letter before or after the consonant. Thus *hyaku* becomes *byaku* and *pyaku*, *ichi* becomes *is*, *sen* becomes *zen*, *roku* becomes *rop*, and *hachi* becomes *hap* and *has*.

2. Once students understand how to construct number words in Japanese, they should be able to interpret the number words on the second page of the handout and to write them in numerals If you wish, students can work in pairs to check each others' answers to these numbers.

ANSWERS

Section 1

23 = nijuusan	28 = nijuuhachi	31 = sanjuuichi
35 = sanjuugo	43 = yonjuusan	46 = yonjuuroku
57 = gojuunana	59 = gojuukyuu	62 = rokujuuni
66 = rokujuuroku	71 = nanajuuichi	75 = nanajuugo
82 = hachijuuni	88 = hachijuuhachi	94 = kyuujuuyon
96 = kyuujuuroku		

Section 2

When *juu, hyaku, sen,* or *man* has a smaller numeral before it, you multiply the two, *nijuu* is (2 × 10), or 20. When *juu, hyaku, sen,* or *man* has a smaller numeral after it, you add the two; *juuni* is (10 + 2), or 12. When *juu, hyaku, sen,* or *man* has one smaller numeral before it and another after it, you multiply by the first and add the second, *nijuuichi* is (2 × 10) + 1, or 21. *Note:* A version of *ichi* may not be used with the exponents of ten. Thus *sen* and *issen* both mean 1,000, and *man* is the root word for ten thousand.

Section 3

Hyphens are used to distinguish between place values. Unhyphenated words are to have mathematical processes applied to them. Commas are used when more than one multiplier is to be used with the multiple of ten. Thus *juu, kyuuman* means (10 × 10,000), (9 × 10,000) or 100,000 + 90,000 or 190,000.

Section 4

(a) nihyaku-yonjuu-nana = 247

(b) happyaku-gojuu-yon = 854

(c) sanzen-roppyaku-nanajuu-hachi = 3,678

(d) juu,kyuuman-issen-kyuuhyaku-rokujuu-go = 191,965

BONUS QUESTION

The answer is ten million. If students have grasped the pattern of how Japanese number words are formed, they should see that *issenman* is one × one thousand × ten thousand, or ten million.

VARIATIONS

- Have students work in small cooperative groups to find the patterns for forming Japanese number words, then break the groups into paies to do the activities.
- Encourage students to translate Japanese number words in terms of exponents, for example, *issenman* = one × one thousand × ten thousand = $1 \times 10^3 \times 10^4 = 10^7$.

- When student pairs have checked each others' answers to the questions on the handout, direct them to create four numbers using Japanese number words, then trade papers with their partners and write their partner's numbers out in numerals.

EXTENSION ACTIVITIES

The Hon, mai, ken: Counting Things in Japanese activity examines another aspect of counting in Japanese, and is an excellent follow-up to this activity.

ASSESSMENT

Were students able to correctly read Japanese number words as numerals? Did students identify the patterns used in forming number words? On the bonus question, were students able to apply what they knew about Japanese number words to decipher an unknown word combination?

Ichi, ni, san, yon, go: Counting in Japanese

The number words we use in English seem to follow several different rules. You need to learn 28 separate words to count from zero to 99. The Japanese system for writing numbers as words is very orderly. In Japanese, you only need to learn 11 number words to count to 99 You can combine those 11 words to make all the number words you need.

1. This table shows most of the Japanese number words for zero to ninety-nine Can you see the pattern used to form them? Once you have found the pattern, fill in the missing number words.

0	1	2	3	4	5	6	7	8	9
zero	ichi	ni	san	yon	go	roku	nana	hachi	kyuu
10	**11**	**12**	**13**	**14**	**15**	**16**	**17**	**18**	**19**
juu	juujichi	juuni	juusan	juuyon	juugo	juuroku	juunana	juuhachi	juukyuu
20	**21**	**22**	**23**	**24**	**25**	**26**	**27**	**28**	**29**
nijuu	nijuuichi	nijuuni	_____	nijuuyon	nijuugo	nijuuroku	nijuunana	_____	nijuukyuu
30	**31**	**32**	**33**	**34**	**35**	**36**	**37**	**38**	**39**
sanjuu	_____	sanjuuni	sanjuusan	sanjuuyon	_____	sanjuuroku	sanjuunana	sanjuuhachi	sanjuukyuu
40	**41**	**42**	**43**	**44**	**45**	**46**	**47**	**48**	**49**
yonjuu	yonjuuichi	yonjuuni	_____	yonjuuyon	yonjuugo	_____	yonjuunana	yonjuuhachi	yonjuukyuu
50	**51**	**52**	**53**	**54**	**55**	**56**	**57**	**58**	**59**
gojuu	gojuuichi	gojuuni	gojuusan	gojuugo	gojuugo	gojuuroku	_____	gojuuhachi	_____
60	**61**	**62**	**63**	**64**	**65**	**66**	**67**	**68**	**69**
rokujuu	rokujuuichi	_____	rokujuusan	rokujuuyon	rokujuugo	_____	rokujuunana	rokujuuhachi	rokujuukyuu
70	**71**	**72**	**73**	**74**	**75**	**76**	**77**	**78**	**79**
nanajuu	_____	nanajuuni	nanajuusan	nanajuuyon	_____	nanajuuroku	nanajuunana	nanajuuhachi	nanajuukyuu
80	**81**	**82**	**83**	**84**	**85**	**86**	**87**	**88**	**89**
hachijuu	hachijuuichi	_____	hachijuusan	hachijuuyon	hachijuugo	hachijuuroku	hachijuunana	_____	hachijuukyuu
90	**91**	**92**	**93**	**94**	**95**	**96**	**97**	**98**	**99**
kyuujuu	kyuujuuichi	kyuujuuni	kyuujuusan	_____	kyuujuugo	_____	kyuujuunana	kyuujuuhachi	kyuujuukyu

23. _____   28. _____   31. _____

35. _____   43. _____   46. _____

57. _____   59. _____   62. _____

66. _____   71 _____   75. _____

82. _____   88 _____   94. _____

96. _____

(continued)

Hands-on Culture of Japan

Ichi, ni, san, yon, go: Counting in Japan *(continued)*

2. Here are the Japanese number words for hundreds, thousands, and so on, up to one million. Can you describe the pattern for forming these words?

   _____

100 hyaku	200 nihyaku	300 sanbyaku	400 yonhyaku	500 gohyaku	600 roppyaku	700 nanahyaku	800 happyaku	900 kyuuhyaku
1000 sen	2000 nisen	3000 sanzen	4000 yonsen	5000 gosen	6000 rokusen	7000 nanasen	8000 hassen	9000 kyuusen
10,000 ichiman	20,000 niman	30,000 sanman	40,000 yonman	50,000 goman	60,000 rokuman	70,000 nanaman	80,000 hachiman	90,000 kyuuman
100,000 juuman	200,000 nijuuman	300,000 sanjuuman	400,000 yonjuuman	500,000 gojuuman	600,000 rokujuuman	700,000 nanajuuman	800,000 hachijuuman	900,000 kyuujuuman
1,000,000 hyakuman	2,000,000 nihyakuman	3,000,000 sanbyakuman	4,000,000 yonhyakuman	5,000,000 gohyakuman	6,000,000 roppyakuman	7,000,000 nanhyakuman	8,000,000 happyakuman	9,000,000 kyuuhyakuman

3. Here are some numbers written in Japanese number words and in numerals. Why do you think some of them have hyphens between compounded number words, and some don't?

   juuroku = 16
   kyuujuuni = 92
   hyaku-nijuu-san = 123
   sanbyaku-kyuujuu-nana = 397
   yonman-gosen-gohyaku-juu-roku = 45,516
   kyuuhyaku,hachijuu,rokuman-yonsen-hyaku-yonjuu-ichi = 9,864,141

   _____

   _____

4. Use the tables and your understanding of the pattern of Japanese number words to read these numbers. Write out their equivalents in Arabic numerals.

   (a) nihyaku-yonjuu-nana = _____   (b) happyaku-gojuu-yon = _____

   (c) sanzen-roppyaku-
       nanajuu-hachi = _____   (d) juu,kyuuman-issen-kyuuh
                                                 yaku-rokujuu-go = _____

Bonus question

   This number isn't explained on the tables above. Can you figure out what it is?

issenman= _____

Hon, mai, ken: Counting Things in Japanese

OBJECTIVES

Math

- Students will explore basic algebraic concepts by adding and subtracting unfamiliar number/unit combinations.

- Students will understand that different words or symbols can be used for numbers, but that the numbers themselves will still perform in the same way.

Social Studies

- Students will understand how different cultures can construct different variants of a similar system.

Art

- Students will associate symbols with concepts, and will practice recognizing concepts from their symbols.

MATERIALS

Hon, mai, ken: Counting Things in Japanese handout
paper
pencils
pens

PREPARATION

The preceding activity on simple counting in Japanese (Ichi, ni, san, yon, go) is not a prerequisite for doing this activity, but it serves as a good introduction to the subject.

PROCEDURE

1. Distribute the handout and discuss with students the concept of using different words to count different objects. Have students brainstorm possible advantages and disadvantages of such a system.

2 Give students time to familiarize themselves with the Japanese symbols for the digits and the units for counting some types of objects. Then have them complete the activity as directed on the handout.

ANSWERS

1. eight people

2. three buildings

3. six cylindrical objects

4. 五本 + 四本 = 九本

5. 七軒 + 三軒 = 十軒

6. 二枚 + 二枚 = 四枚

EXTENSION ACTIVITIES

- If we wanted to use a similar system of counting objects in English, what kinds of groupings would be most useful—groupings of round objects, flat objects, mechanical objects? Have students work in groups to devise a counting system that combines number words with short words to indicate the type of object being counted. A spokesperson from each group explains that group's system to the class.

- Have students work in small groups to prepare five simple addition or subtraction problems, using *kanji*. Groups then trade problems and solve the problems they are given.

ASSESSMENT

Did students correctly associate symbols with words and numbers?

Hon, mai, ken: Counting Things in Japanese

Like English, the Japanese language has a system of number words. But the Japanese system for counting is very different from ours. The biggest difference in the Japanese system is that the number word is usually combined with an ending. These endings, called classifiers, show what kind of thing is being counted. It's similar to the way we say, in English, "three *sheets* of paper" or "seven *head* of cattle" One word is used when counting cylindrical objects. Another is used when counting thin, flat objects. And still another word is used to count miscellaneous things.

But in Japanese the number word and the classifier become one word, like three-sheets or seven-head. As in English, another noun is usually added to say exactly what is being counted. The classifier just gives the general type of object. So if you wanted to say "three pencils," you would say "three-cylinders of pencils."

When these words are written in Japanese, a writing symbol called a *kanji* is used for each word. Here are the kanji that stand for the numbers from one to ten

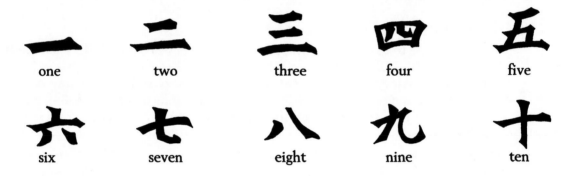

一	二	三	四	五
one	two	three	four	five

六	七	八	九	十
six	seven	eight	nine	ten

Here are the symbols for some units of counting objects, and the type of objects they are used for.

hon—with long cylindrical objects

mai—with sheetlike things

ken—with buildings

nin—with more than three people

(continued)

Hon, mai, ken: Counting Things in Japanese *(continued)*

Even though these symbols don't look like numbers, you can use them in mathematical processes. In English you might say·

one bottle + three bottles = four bottles

In Japanese characters, the same statement might look like this:

一本 + 三本 = 四本

Here are some examples of combinations of number words and counting units

五人 = five people

三本 = three cylindrical objects

Use the symbols to figure out how many things these character groups refer to, and what kinds of things.

1. 八人   2. 三軒   3. 六本

_____   _____   _____

Write the Japanese characters for these simple sums, including the answers

4 Five bottles + four bottles =

_____

5. Seven houses + three houses =

_____

6. Two sheets of paper + two sheets of paper =

_____

Making Paper

OBJECTIVES

Art

• Students will understand some of the characteristics of a medium.

Social Studies/Science

• Students will understand that some resources can be recycled, not discarded.

MATERIALS

old paper—office paper, newspaper, construction paper, paper
   towels, etc.
blender
large pan or tub
wooden frame that will fit easily in the tub—5 × 7 or 6 × 9 inches are
   convenient sizes
nylon or aluminum window screening mesh
staple gun or nails
food coloring
leaves, dried flowers, gold and silver leaf, other decorative materials
   to embed in the paper
felt blotters or old towels
sponges
optional: an iron

PROCEDURE

1. Cut a piece of screening to cover the top of the
   wooden frame, and staple or nail it to the frame.
   This will be your paper mold. You can prepare
   one frame for the whole class, or divide the class
   into groups and prepare one frame for each
   group. Since this activity is always popular, you
   might want to prepare several frames.

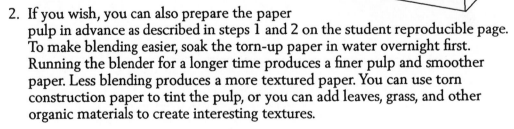

2. If you wish, you can also prepare the paper
   pulp in advance as described in steps 1 and 2 on the student reproducible page.
   To make blending easier, soak the torn-up paper in water overnight first.
   Running the blender for a longer time produces a finer pulp and smoother
   paper. Less blending produces a more textured paper. You can use torn
   construction paper to tint the pulp, or you can add leaves, grass, and other
   organic materials to create interesting textures.

3. Give the students the handout on making paper, and guide them through the process it describes. Stress the importance of stirring the solution each time the frame is lowered into it so that the pulp remains suspended in the solution. They must also keep the frame level as it is raised so that the paper is not thicker on one side than the other. If the layer of pulp tears when the frame is being removed, just add it back into the solution.

4. Students can add elements like leaves, dried flowers, and bits of gold leaf to the solution, or they can embed them in the pulp while it is on the frame or on the blotter. Encourage students to see the paper they are making as a piece of art in its own right, not just the base for a future project.

5. The paper can simply be left on the blotter to dry, or you can speed up the process with an iron. Cover the paper with a second blotter or towel, then iron through this covering layer until the paper is dry. The blotters get soaked quite quickly, so make sure you have plenty

VARIATION

• A neater finished product can be produced by using a deckle as well as the paper mold. For this, you will need a second wooden frame the same size as the first. This frame should not be covered with screening. Its only function is to contain the pulp at the edges. To use, hold the paper mold with the screen side up, then place the second frame (the deckle) on top of the mold Then proceed as directed in the handout.

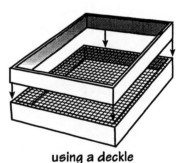

using a deckle

• To create paper shapes, place cookie cutters or stencils on top of the mesh, then pour pulp into the opening in the top of the cookie cutter. Proceed through the other steps as usual.

EXTENSION ACTIVITIES

Students can use their handmade paper as the base for a calligraphy project, to make greeting cards, to make a Japanese fan, for the linoleum block print project on page 14, or to make a cover for the folded book project on page 50.

ASSESSMENT

Did students successfully make at least one sheet of paper?

Name _____   Date _____

Making Paper

Traditional Japanese paper, called *washi*, is made from the soft inner bark of plants. Because this paper is both soft and strong, it can be used in many ways. Brightly colored and decorated paper is used in origami, or paper-folding. For centuries, intricately cut paper stencils were used to print Japanese fabric. Calligraphy, or decorative writing, is often done on handmade paper. Folding screens and sliding room partitions are covered in paper. Fans and umbrellas are made of paper

Making handmade paper from raw materials calls for chemicals. But you can use a simpler method to recycle used paper into your own handmade paper.

1 Tear used paper into small pieces.

2 Put about two cups of water in a blender and turn it on at low speed. Slowly add a few cups of torn paper. Don't add it all at once—it will jam the blades of the blender Increase the speed of the blender to high, and blend for about a minute

3. Half fill a basin with water, and add the paper pulp to the water.

4. Hold the papermaking frame so that the screen side faces up. Slide it into the pan. With the frame in the pan, stir the solution so that the pulp stays suspended and doesn't all sink to the bottom.

5 Slowly, keeping it level, bring the frame straight up to the surface of the water. A layer of pulp will collect on the screen, while the water drains through

6 Turn the frame over onto a blotter or old towel so that the pulp is pressed against the fabric. Press a sponge against the back of the screen to remove excess water.

7 Starting at one corner, so that it comes up at an angle, lift the frame from the pulp

8 Let your paper dry, then use it in any way you like!

                                       Hands-on Culture of Japan

A Game of Go

OBJECTIVES

Math

- Students will apply knowledge of measurement and spatial relations to solving a concrete problem.

Social Studies

- Students will create and use a popular game from another culture.

Art

- Students will use knowledge of drafting and spatial relations to create a game board.

MATERIALS

For each game board:

A Game of Go handout

square of poster board or wood—12" × 12" works well

181 black and 180 white disks, about $\frac{1}{2}$" in diameter (buttons, beads, or paper discs work well)

pencils, pens, and markers

a selection of measuring and drafting tools for students to choose from, including ruler, protractor, set square

PROCEDURE

This activity can be done by individual students, in student pairs, or with small groups of four to six students. Divide students into groups, if desired, and pass out the handout. You may want to demonstrate the basic moves on an overhead or on the blackboard. Then distribute materials to student groups. The challenge in making the board is to divide the area up evenly and keep all the lines parallel. Encourage students to come up with strategies for doing this in advance.

Once all student groups have completed a go board, have students try playing the game. For more information on playing Go and on Go strategies, many publications are available. Many areas have Go clubs, whose members are often willing to explain the game and demonstrate strategies.

BONUS QUESTION

There are 361 points. Students will probably multiply the number of horizontal lines by the number of vertical lines to find the answer. Adding the number of black stones (181) and the number of white stones (180) will also give the answer, but the student handout does not mention that there is a stone for every point.

VARIATIONS

Another game, *gomokunarabe*, is played with the same board and pieces as Go, but it is much simpler. The aim of gomokunarabe is to arrange five stones in a row. It is harder than it looks, but requires far less skill and strategy than Go, and so is more suitable for most middle-grade students

ASSESSMENT

Did students create a game board with the correct number of lines, evenly spaced? Is the finished product neat and attractive?

A Game of Go

Go, a game for two players, is probably the most popular board game in Japan. The game began in China around 2356 B.C. and came to Japan around A.D. 500. The rules of the game are very simple, but the game itself calls for a lot of skill.

How to Play

Go is played on a square game board with small round stones—181 stones for Black, and 180 for White. The board is marked off with 19 vertical lines and 19 horizontal ones. The game focuses on the points where these lines meet. The player with the black stones goes first, and places a stone on any intersection point. Then the player with White places a stone, again on any intersection point. The aim of the game is to surround empty points with stones of one color—while keeping your opponent from controlling any empty points.

Capturing Enemy Stones

To keep your opponent from controlling points, you can capture enemy stones and remove them from the board. To do this, the enemy stones must be completely surrounded by stones of your color with no empty points beside them in a row or column. Empty points on the diagonal don't count.

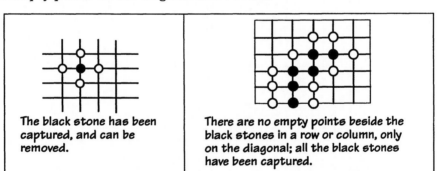

The black stone has been captured, and can be removed.

There are no empty points beside the black stones in a row or column, only on the diagonal; all the black stones have been captured.

Moving onto a Point Surrounded by Enemy Stones

If a point is surrounded by enemy stones, a player can only place a stone on the point if the move captures enemy stones.

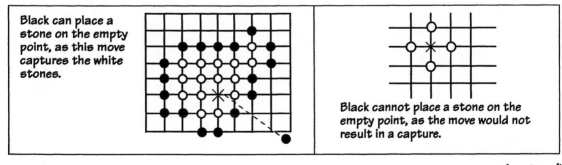

Black can place a stone on the empty point, as this move captures the white stones.

Black cannot place a stone on the empty point, as the move would not result in a capture.

(continued)

A Game of Go *(continued)*

Scoring

To score, add up the number of points each player has captured by surrounding the opponent's pieces with stones. Then subtract the number of pieces that player has lost. Subtract the number of captured pieces from the number of points controlled. The player with the highest final score wins.

Make Your Own Go Board

 Using the description of a Go board, create a Go board of your own. Remember, the board must be square and have 19 horizontal and 19 vertical lines (including the outer edges of the square). The spaces between all the lines should be exactly the same. When you have made your board, try playing a game of Go!

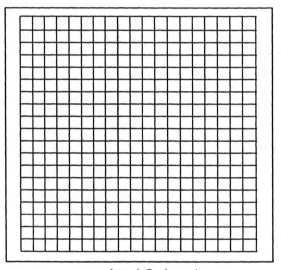

completed Go board

Bonus question

Without counting the points, answer this question: If there are 19 horizontal lines and 19 vertical lines, how many points—line intersections—are there? How did you get your answer?

_____

_____

Mon: Heraldic Crests

Teacher Guide Page

OBJECTIVES

Social Studies

• Students will see how different cultures can express a similar need.

Art

• Students will design graphic symbols to represent some aspect of themselves or their families.

MATERIALS

Mon: Heraldic Crests handout
white paper
colored construction paper
pencils
scissors, compasses and protractors
rulers

PROCEDURE

1. Distribute the handout and initiate a discussion of symbols. At the idea-generating stage, it can be helpful to have students work in small groups to brainstorm possible symbols. Good starting points include sports, hobbies, ethnic background, an initial from a name, and the original meaning of a family name.

2. Once students have chosen a symbol, they should work individually to simplify it.

3. The final step is to cut the symbol out of one piece of construction paper, either dark or light, and mount it on a piece of contrasting paper. Since indigo blue and white are very common colors for Japanese fabric printing, you might want to have students use only navy and white, then display the completed mon in the classroom.

VARIATION

• Have students include a one-sentence explanation of their symbols and why they chose them.

• Have students work in groups to design a mon for your class or school, then display the completed mon in the classroom.

EXTENSION ACTIVITY

Have students use the mon they designed in this activity as the stencil design in the Katazome: Stencil Dyeing activity on page 45.

ASSESSMENT

Did students create a simple graphic design, cut it out, and mount it on contrasting paper? Is the finished product visually appealing?

Mon: Heraldic Crests

Japanese society in the medieval period had a lot in common with medieval European society. Both were feudal societies: A rich ruling class held all the land and let other people use it in return for their services. And both societies developed a system of heraldry, or symbols used to identify people and families. The European system was very complicated, with its own special vocabulary. The Japanese system was much simpler.

Beginning in the eleventh century, high-ranking Japanese families began using one specific design on their most formal clothes. Soon these designs came to be used as symbols for the family name. The designs, called *mon*, or crests, were used on clothes, carriages, banners and screens, furniture, and weapons. Many of the designs were based on elegant natural forms: wisteria, peonies, irises, and cranes. One flower—the chrysanthemum—was reserved for the emperor.

Unlike European crests, Japanese mon were usually very graphic, well suited for stenciling on fabric. They were often enclosed in a circle, a square, or a hexagon. The symbol was usually chosen because it had some kind of meaning, a connection with the family or the family's name.

In this activity, you are going to design a mon, or heraldic crest, for yourself or your family.

1. Start by thinking of things that are special or important to you or to your family. Then look for some aspect of those things that you could use in your design. For example, you might decide that baseball is one of your family's most important activities. In that case, you might use a baseball or a pair of crossed baseball bats or a catcher's mitt as the basis of your design.

(continued)

Mon: Heraldic Crests *(continued)*

2. Once you have decided on a symbol to use in your design, try to simplify it as much as possible. The symbols you see at the top of this page are Japanese mon. Do you see how much they have been simplified? There are very few details in the pictures, so that the image is as clear as possible. Take out as much detail as you possibly can. Your symbol should show the essence of the thing, not a detailed picture.

3. When you have finalized your design, transfer it onto a sheet of construction paper. Make your design the size of the full sheet of paper.

4. Finally, cut your design out of the construction paper and mount it on a sheet of paper of a contrasting color. Effective color combinations include navy blue with white, purple with yellow, white with black, or you can choose a combination of your own.

Katazome: Stencil Dyeing

Teacher
Guide
Page

OBJECTIVES

Social Studies

• Students will use a traditional art medium from another culture to express an aspect of their lives.

Art

• Students will create a two-color resist print using positive and negative space.

MATERIALS

For each student or student group:

Katazome: Stencil Dyeing handout

precut 12" × 12" square of 100 percent cotton cloth

starch resist paste (makes $1\frac{1}{4}$ cups): 1 tbsp cornstarch, 1 tbsp white wheat flour, 1 tbsp rice flour, 1 tbsp laundry starch, $\frac{1}{2}$ tsp alum

newspapers

waxed kitchen paper

cardboard rectangle, about 2" × 4", to use as spreader

plastic squeeze bottle (clean, empty mustard bottle or other similar bottle)

precut 12" × 12" square of contact paper

sketch paper

pencils

fabric dye and dye bath or fabric paints

optional: mon designs from Mon: Heraldic Crests activity on page 40

BACKGROUND

Resist dyeing is a dyeing technique that involves protecting an area of fabric with a medium that resists dye, then dyeing the fabric. When the resist medium is removed, the treated area remains the original color, while the rest of the fabric takes on the color of the dye bath. This is a sophisticated version of making a drawing with a crayon, then painting over the drawing with a water-based paint; the wax crayon resists the paint, and only the unwaxed areas take the color. The art of batik is another version of resist dyeing.

The resist method described here can be used freehand to create individual pieces of fabric, but in combination with a stencil it is more often used to create fabrics with a repeating pattern.

PREPARATION

1. Prepare the resist paste. Dissolve all the ingredients but the alum in one cup of cold water. Stir with a wooden spoon to break up any lumps. Heat in a double boiler, stirring constantly, until the mixture appears clear. The mixture should be about the consistency of honey; add more water if necessary to thin the paste. Add the alum and stir thoroughly. The paste can be refrigerated, but it should be warmed gently before using.

2. Cut the 100 percent cotton fabric and contact paper into 12" × 12" squares. If contact paper shows a tendency to curl up, place the squares under a weight to flatten them before using.

PROCEDURE

1. Students create a simple graphic design as described on the handout. If students have already done the Mon: Heraldic Crests activity on page 40, they may use the mon they designed for this activity; that design should already be simplified enough to be appropriate for stencil cutting. Remind students that small, fiddly design elements may be lost in the printing process. A simple graphic design is most suitable for this technique.

2. Students transfer their designs to contact paper and cut out the stencils, then prepare for stenciling as described in steps 2 to 4 of the student handout. You may wish to have students form small groups for the stenciling process.

3. Gently warm the resist paste before use. If you do not have access to a stove or microwave oven, you can do this by putting the paste container in a pan of hot tap water, changing the water for fresh hot water as needed until the paste is warm. Since this can take time, start the process well before you need the paste.

4. Put a small amount of warm paste in each squeeze bottle. Students squeeze the bottle gently to extrude paste onto the fabric. Remind them to be careful—squeeze too hard and too much paste will rush out. Demonstrate this technique for the class.

5. (a) To protect your classroom—and your students' clothes—you may want to do the dyeing part of this project outside the classroom. Dyes for use with both hot and cold water are readily available from art supplies. Whether you do the dyeing in the classroom or outside it, follow the manufacturer's directions for dyeing the fabric and setting the color, if needed.

   or

   (b) Instead of using a dye bath for the fabric squares, thin fabric paint until it flows easily, then brush onto the fabric. Follow the manufacturer's directions to set the color, then rinse and dry the fabric as described on the handout.

VARIATIONS

- Instead of making your own resist paste, use a commercial fabric resist, then proceed as directed.

- Use watercolor paper or rice paper instead of fabric and a watercolor resist medium like frisket instead of starch. Make a stencil of newsprint or other soft, absorbent paper. Attach the stencil firmly to the watercolor or rice paper at the corners Apply the resist medium to the exposed paper with a stiff brush, being careful not to get any under the edges of the stencil. Remove the stencil and let the resist dry, then brush the paper with colored ink or watercolor paint to cover the untreated areas. When the print is dry, remove the resist medium following manufacturer's directions.

EXTENSION ACTIVITY

- Sew fabric squares together in strips or blocks to create a border around the classroom, or as a classroom quilt.

- There are several easy ways to make stenciled cloths into attractive cushions. (1) Bind the edges of the fabric square and sew it onto a larger premade cushion (2) Take a second piece of 12" × 12" cloth. With the right sides of both pieces of fabric together, sew around three outer edges of the square and partway around the fourth side. Turn the case right side out by pulling the fabric through the gap in the fourth side. Fill with pillow stuffing, then hand stitch the opening that remains.

ASSESSMENT

Did students create a graphic design appropriate for stenciling? Did students cut and use the stencil effectively?

Katazome: Stencil Dyeing

When Japan was again opened to the West in the late 1800's, Japanese stencils for fabric printing were among the many objects that fascinated and baffled the West The stencils were made of paper, and many of them were very complex, with a number of fine details. On stencils with large open areas or particularly delicate details, the open area was filled with a web of fine threads. These threads served to strengthen the stencil and keep it from tearing when it was used, but they were so fine that the printing ink flowed around them; they didn't show up in the final print.

It looked as if the threads were sandwiched between two layers of paper, but Westerners couldn't figure out how it was done. The threads couldn't be inserted before the stencil was cut, because then they would be cut away with the excess paper But the registration of the two layers of paper was so precise that it seemed they must have been glued together before being cut

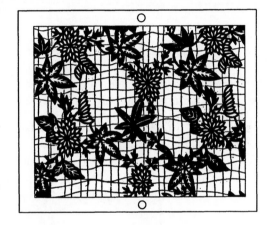

The answer to this puzzle was surprisingly simple. The stencil cutter would first place the stencil design on top of four or six sheets of paper. The next step would be to punch a small hole through all the layers at either the top or bottom of the sheet, outside the design area. These small holes were used later as registration marks, to match up two cut stencils. Then the artisan would cut the design through all the layers of paper, making four or six identical copies of the stencil.

For the next step, two sheets were dampened slightly. One sheet was laid down flat and coated with glue. Fine silk reinforcing threads were laid on top of this sheet. They formed a grid, with their ends extending onto the margins of the design. Then the second stencil sheet was laid carefully over the first, with pins in the registration holes. The pins could only go through the holes in both sheets when both were perfectly aligned with each other. The stencil, with its reinforcing threads, was ready for use.

There were two common methods for printing fabric. The first was the direct method. Using this method, the printer placed the stencil on the fabric, then squeezed ink over it. The ink went through the cut areas of the stencil onto the fabric. The areas behind the stencil stayed white.

In the indirect method, or resist method, the printer placed the stencil on the fabric as before. Then, instead of ink, the exposed surfaces of the fabric were covered with a paste made of starch. Once this paste had dried, the fabric was dyed. The areas coated with starch resisted the dye and stayed white. The areas not covered with

(continued)

Katazome: Stencil Dyeing *(continued)*

starch took the dye. The resulting print was exactly the opposite of the print in the direct method, where the cut areas of the stencil took the color and the areas behind the paper stayed white.

In this activity, you will create a stencil and use the paste-resist method to dye a piece of cloth—but the approach you use for your stencil will be much simpler than the traditional Japanese one!

1. First, prepare a design you would like to print on a piece of fabric You will be working with a piece of fabric 12" × 12", and your design should use the entire area In the finished print, the areas you cut away will be light, and the areas where paper remains will be dark.

   The design should consist of fairly simple shapes, without many fine details This printing method is not suitable for thin lines or small objects. You should also make sure that all the elements of your design are connected to each other.

This design can't be cut from a single stencil, as the square in the middle will just fall away when it's cut out.

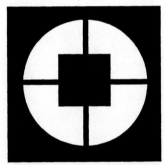

The "bridges" connecting the inner square to the outer circle mean that this design will stay in one piece when cut.

2. Once you have finished your design, transfer it to a 12" × 12" sheet of contact paper. No, contact paper isn't a traditional part of this technique, but this way you won't need to worry as much about tearing the stencil, or getting the starch resist under the stencil's edges. Remember that the areas you cut away will be white on the finished print, and the areas you leave will be dark. Cut the stencil out of the contact paper.

(continued)

Katazome: Stencil Dyeing *(continued)*

3. Make a pad of newspaper about two feet square (24" × 24"). Cover the newspaper with waxed paper. Now, tape the fabric to the top of the pad. The tape should pull the fabric smooth against the paper, without wrinkles or loose areas.

4. Carefully peel the backing paper off your stencil and apply it to the fabric. It may be easiest to start peeling the paper away from one corner and place that corner against a corner of the fabric, then peel the rest of the paper away from underneath, lowering the stencil against the cloth as you go.

5. Pour a small amount of the resist paste into the open areas of the stencil. Use the cardboard spreader to spread the paste across all the exposed areas of fabric. Be careful not to force paste under the edges of the stencil.

6. Let the paste dry for a few minutes. Then carefully peel the contact paper stencil away from the fabric. Hang the fabric to finish drying.

7. When the resist paste is fully dry, dye or paint the fabric as directed by your teacher.

8. To remove paste and excess dye, rinse the fabric until the water runs clear. Hang it up to dry. Your stencil-printed fabric is ready to mount or frame.

Making a Folded Paper Book

OBJECTIVES

Math

• Students will apply precise measuring skills to the creation of an object.

Social Studies

• Students will explore some of the ways in which different cultures develop resources.

Art

• Students will create and decorate a handmade paper book.

MATERIALS

roll of unglazed white paper
lightweight card stock
handmade paper from Making Paper activity on page 34, or other decorated paper, or plain paper and materials to decorate it
rulers
pencils
construction paper
white glue
yarn, or colored string, or fabric ribbon
hole punch

PREPARATION

Cut strips of 9" × 96" paper from the paper roll. Cut the card into $9\frac{1}{2} \times 6\frac{1}{2}$" rectangles. Cut yarn or string into 12" lengths. Each book will require one paper strip, two pieces of card stock, and one length of yarn or string.

PROCEDURE

1. If students have not made their own paper in the activity on page 34 and you do not wish to use other already decorated paper, give students plain paper to decorate and decorating supplies. Suitable materials include brushes and paint, collage materials, and simple printmaking materials like potato slices and cut erasers. Explain to students that they will be using this decorated paper for the front and back covers of their books, so they should make it as attractive as possible.

2. Distribute the handout and go through the procedure with students. Point out that the measuring and folding step is critical. If all the segments of paper are not properly cut and all the folds are not absolutely straight, the finished book

will be clumsy looking and unattractive. Distribute materials. Students then proceed as directed on the handout.

VARIATIONS

- Some students may find the accurate folding of this method too challenging. A slight mistake on the first fold will be exaggerated on subsequent folds, and the finished product may not resemble a book at all. You can use this variant with the whole class, or only with less dexterous students who would be certain to be frustrated by the project otherwise.

- Instead of using one long sheet of paper, this method uses five sheets of 9" × 12" paper and two sheets of 9" × 18" paper. The student folds each of the 9" × 12" sheets in half to create the middle pages of the book, then folds the 9" × 18" sheets in thirds to create the end pages, with an extra leaf to glue to the covers. The book is then assembled as shown in the diagram. The holes are punched and the book is threaded as described in steps 6 and 7 on the handout.

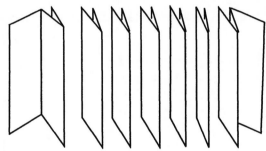

EXTENSION ACTIVITIES

Have students use their folded books with either the haiku activity on page 54 or the proverb activity on page 65. Once their writing is completed, they should carefully write their finished pieces in the folded book. Some pages can be used for drawings to illustrate the poems or folktale.

BONUS QUESTION

Point out to students that they started off with a strip of paper 9" high and 96" long, and ended up with sixteen 6" × 9" pages. If they wanted a book with eight 8" × 10" pages, what size strip would they need to start off with? (10" × 64") What about a book with twenty 4" × 5" pages? (5" × 80") Would it be possible to make a book with 13 pages? Why not? (Because the last leaf on each end must face in the same direction to be attached to the covers. If the book had an uneven number of pages, the back cover couldn't be attached.)

ASSESSMENT

Did students produce a neat, accurately folded book?

Name _____ Date _____

Making a Folded Paper Book

Thousands of years ago, in various parts of the world, different societies developed writing systems and materials to write on. But they didn't write books—or not what we would call books today. Most cultures did their early writing on long, narrow strips of cloth or paper, called scrolls. Scrolls were rolled up for storage To read a scroll, you would start at one end and unroll a little bit at a time, rolling up the part you had just read as you went along.

Books were a later development. A book consists of a number of leaves of paper joined together along one edge and bound between two covers. Most books today are made, or bound, by machines. But some very fine books are still made by hand

In this activity you will use a Japanese method to create a hand-bound book. You will fold a long strip of paper up like an accordion, then attach the folds together at one edge to make a book.

1. Fold the long paper strip every 6 inches, with one fold going forward and one going backward, like a fan Accurate measuring and folding are important here If any of your folds are crooked or if the pages aren't exactly the same size, the finished book won't be very nice looking.

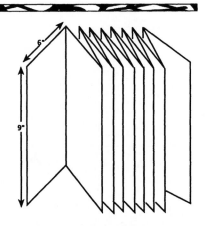

2. To make a cover, take two pieces of 8½" × 11" decorated paper If your decorated paper is smaller than 8½" × 11", glue the decorated paper to the center of a sheet of 8½" × 11" construction paper. Place the decorated piece of paper facedown on your work surface. Draw a straight line 1 inch from each edge. You should have a rectangle 6½" × 8½" Spread white glue on this inner rectangle. Carefully position one of the pieces of card stock on the glued area and press it in place Cut off the corners of the decorated paper at a 45-degree angle.

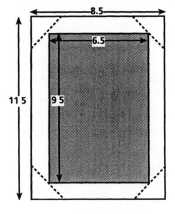

(continued)

Making a Folded Paper Book (continued)

3. Fold the edges of the decorated paper over the card stock and glue in place.

4. Place one cover at each end of the folded strip of paper. The pages should be centered on the height of the covers so that the covers stick out $\frac{1}{4}$" above and below the pages. The back long edge of the folded paper—the spine of the book—should be even with the back edges of the covers. The front edge of the covers should stick out $\frac{1}{2}$" beyond the pages.

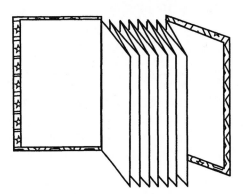

5. Glue the first 6-inch panel of the folded paper to the inside of the front cover. Glue the last 6-inch panel to the back cover.

6. In three stages, punch holes along the spine of the book, $\frac{1}{2}$" in from the edge. One hole will be 2" down from the top of the book and one will be 2" up from the bottom. Because the book is so thick, you will need to punch the pages and the covers separately. With a pencil, lightly mark where the holes should go on the front cover. With the book open, punch these holes through the cover. Then close the book and mark the position of the holes on the first page by drawing through the cover holes with a pencil. Punch the holes through the inner pages. Mark the position of the holes in the back cover, and punch. All three sets of holes must be perfectly aligned.

7. Thread a piece of yarn or colored string through the holes with the ends at the front of the book. Tie with a bow knot. Your bookbinding project is complete.

Haiku

OBJECTIVES

Language Arts

- Students will write a brief poem following a strict form.
- Students will create sensory images.

Social Studies

- Students will appreciate that simple-seeming developments in another culture are often more complex than they appear.

Art

- Students will connect words with visual and tactile images.

MATERIALS

Haiku handout
paper and pencils

PROCEDURE

Distribute the handout and go through it with the class. If you wish, read some examples of haiku, or write some on the board to serve as models. A few are included here for your use, or you may choose others from books of haiku. Students should proceed as directed on the handout.

Temple bells die out.
The fragrant blossoms remain.
A perfect evening!
—*Matsuo Basho (1644–1694)*

On the wide seashore
a stray blossom and the shells
make one drifting sand
—*Matsuo Basho (1644–1694)*

A giant firefly:
that way, this way, that way, this—
and it passes by.
        —*Issa (1762–1826)*

Amid the falling
of honeysuckle petals
the mosquitoes buzz.
        —*Buson*

BACKGROUND

A haiku is a short poem, the Japanese equivalent of a sonnet. Originally the opening verse of a longer chain of verses, and now considered a complete poem by itself, the haiku has a very simple form: three lines, the first five syllables long, the second seven, and the third five again.

Haiku aim to give an impression of a moment. They often describe daily situations that help the reader see things in a different way. Haiku should include some reference to nature, and to a season of the year. As well as the strictures of length and the connection with the seasons, there are a few general guidelines for haiku. However, since these elements are less important than the idea of expressing a moment, students should only be introduced to them once they have achieved some degree of mastery of the basic haiku form.

One element usually present in classical haiku is a pause or break between the first line and the subsequent two lines. This can be expressed in either a period, a colon, or a dash, but the pause should be more than that indicated by a comma. A second guideline is to avoid making the poem a first-person narrative—I saw, I heard, I felt. While the poem should certainly reflect the individual's point of view, it should also suggest a degree of universality of experience. The third guideline can be more difficult to follow: The use of simile and metaphor should be avoided. You should decide when, and whether, to introduce these elements to your students.

The influence of Zen Buddhism can be seen in the references to nature and the sometimes cryptic meaning of the poems. Many Japanese haiku contain subtle symbolism which is hard for Western readers to fully appreciate.

EXTENSION ACTIVITIES

Have students use the folded paper book activity on page 50 to create their own book of haiku, illustrating the poems on the facing page if they desire.

ASSESSMENT

Did students write poems that met the line and syllable requirements? Did poems use vivid imagery and refer to nature?

Name _____   Date _____

Haiku

Haiku is the name of a Japanese poetic form. Haiku consist of 17 syllables divided into 3 lines. The first line is 5 syllables long, the second is 7, and the third is again 5.

Haiku are very short, and the lines don't rhyme. But haiku aren't all that easy to write. To be really considered a haiku, the poem should capture the feeling of a moment. It should also be connected to nature, and include a reference to one of the seasons of the year. All in just 17 syllables!

The aim of haiku is to record a moment that meant something to the person speaking in the poem. To achieve this effect, don't just state facts. Try to use descriptions that involve the senses. Look at the difference between these two poems.

I	II
It was a nice day.	The sun warmed the grass.
The birds had all hatched their eggs.	Over the lake a swallow
They were free to roam.	flirted with the clouds.

The poem that appeals to the senses of sight and touch seems much more vivid than the one that just gives the bare bones of the information. People who read your poem should get a strong impression of the scene you are trying to show. Think about how things might smell, sound, feel, taste, look. If you include at least one image that appeals to the senses, your poems will be much more vibrant.

How can you make these images also suggest a season of the year? Think of leaves crunching, the smell of smoke in the air, fireflies gleaming in the night, fog drifting over the city.

遂 Now write four haiku, one for each season of the year. Remember the rules of haiku: three lines, 5–7–5, reference to the season, connection with nature. See how much you can say in just a few words.

_____   _____

_____   _____

_____   _____

_____   _____

_____   _____

_____   _____

Zen Gardens of Sand and Stone

OBJECTIVES

Math

- Students will experiment with different combinations of concrete points to form triangles.

Art

- Students will use an unfamiliar medium to create an attractive arrangement within prescribed parameters.

Social Studies

- Students will learn about some of the ways in which Buddhism influenced Japanese culture.

MATERIALS

Gardens of Sand and Stone handout
cardboard shoebox lid or other similar size box with low sides
fine sand (the sand sold for children's sandboxes works well)
rocks and stones, from pebble size to a few inches in diameter
black paint
2-inch sections of wide-toothed comb, or cardboard notched to
   create a toothed effect to make "rakes," as shown at right
spoons and other tools to transfer sand

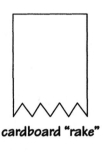

cardboard "rake"

PREPARATION

If you wish, you can paint the outside of the boxes black and fill the boxes with sand, or you can direct students to do this as they start their projects.

PROCEDURE

Distribute the handout and materials. Since it is often hard to convince students that more is not necessarily better, you may wish to give each student no more than three stones. Ask students what they know about Zen Buddhism. If you wish, discuss with them the concept of the *koan*—the short, puzzling questions a Zen master, or *roshi*, often asks students to help lead them to enlightenment. Well-known koans include What is the sound of one hand clapping? and What is *mu* (nothingness)? Students proceed as directed on the handout.

BACKGROUND

Over the years, many design principles for grouping rocks in *kare-sansui* have been developed. Many of the temple gardens designed centuries ago can still be seen in Japan, their sand raked out freshly every day.

ASSESSMENT

Did students use rocks and stones to create a harmonious grouping based on the triangle? Did they use their "rakes" to create interesting patterns in the sand?

Zen Gardens of Sand and Stone

Many aspects of Japanese culture began somewhere else. However, they have become so much a part of Japan that they seem always to have been there The Buddhist faith is one of these cultural imports. Buddhism began in India around 530 B.C., and came to Japan via China around A.D. 550. In Japan it was influenced by Shinto, the ancient religion of Japan, which is still practiced today.

One approach to Buddhism is known as Zen Buddhism. Zen focuses on meditation as the key to understanding the true meaning of Buddha. Buddha's enlightenment came when he saw truths that had always been there, but that he just hadn't seen before. Because this enlightenment came from a sudden flash of insight, Zen masters look for ways to spark that insight in their students. Zen teachers believe that insight can come from many things—from meditation, a single noise, a word, or even an arrangement of rocks. And so the Zen teacher aims to stimulate students until they are open to insight, and to trigger that flash of understanding.

One technique used to do this is visual stimulation. But don't let the word *stimulation* fool you. Zen teachers don't create bright rooms and gardens filled with flowers. They create small, serene gardens that encourage meditation.

One approach to creating this serenity is a style of gardening called *kare-sansui*, or dry landscape. In kare-sansui gardens no trees, flowers, grass, or water are used. They are represented by stones, rocks, and sand Mountains and waterfalls are indicated by rocks and smaller stones. A stream of water is suggested by carefully raking patterns in the sand.

In this activity you will create a miniature kare-sansui garden. Before you begin, think about the effect your garden should have. These gardens are designed to encourage meditation. They are not imitations of landscapes, but abstractions. They are often designed using triangles. Rocks within groupings would be set in triangular relationships to each other and to other groupings. This arrangement was seen as well balanced and harmonious.

 Remembering the triangle design, use the rocks, sand, and "rake" provided to create a restful, serene garden in a shallow box.

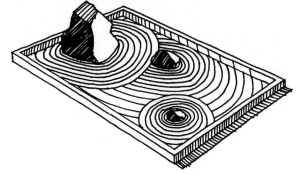

Japanese Writing

OBJECTIVES

Art

• Students will practice using symbols to express ideas.

Social Studies

• Students will understand the basic structure of written Japanese.

Language Arts

• Students will appreciate the difference between an alphabet and a syllabary.

MATERIALS

Japanese Writing handout
paper and pencils

PROCEDURE

Distribute the handout and go over it with students. Allow students time to become familiar with the symbols, then have them proceed as directed.

BACKGROUND

The Chinese script was officially adopted in Japan about the beginning of the fifth century, although it was used by many Japanese long before that time. This adoption is traceable to the third century, but the earliest extant records longer than a few words are from the eighth century. Originally the characters were used to write Chinese, but then they came to symbolize native Japanese words similar in meaning to the Chinese. In this process most of the characters were simplified and made more cursive to the point that in many cases little or nothing is left of their original shape.

Every Chinese character, or *kanji*, can be read in two ways. It can represent a Japanese word that imitates the sound and meaning of the original Chinese, known as the *on* reading, or it can represent a native word of similar meaning, known as the *kun* reading. It is the kun reading that is the accustomed meaning of the character when it is used by itself. Every character also has a third use in which its on or kun sound can be used phonetically to represent a Japanese syllable while abstracting from its on or kun meaning.

Syllabic writing is traceable to the sixth century, when kanji were used as phonograms, but it was not until the ninth century that standardized systems of *kana* began to develop Eventually two different systems of phonetic representation, *hiragana* and *katakana*, emerged.

Until the fifteenth century, Japanese was written in a mixture of *kanji* and *katakana*. At that time the hiragana symbols became the popular and literary medium, with katakana being used for scholarly and practical texts. Present writing is in kanji

and hiragana, the orthography of which has been reformed since World War II
In these reforms the unrestricted use of thousands of kanji characters was limited to a list of 1850 symbols for official and daily use, and their shapes and strokes were greatly simplified. In the early 1980's the number of characters on the list was increased to 1945, and additional character simplifications were adopted. Kana spellings are now based on contemporary pronunciation, in contrast to the prior retention of spellings based on the sound of Late Old Japanese.

Learning kanji is the hardest part of learning to read in Japanese. In the first year of elementary school, students must learn 80 kanji, in the second year 160, in the third year 200, and so on. By the end of their sixth year in school, Japanese students are expected to have memorized 1006 separate kanji.

Hiragana and katakana, the syllabaries, were derived from kanji. Hiragana are used with kanji to write things like verb endings and other grammatical constructions Katakana are used mainly to write foreign words (Strictly speaking, students would not use hiragana for their names, but katakana.) One use for *romaji*, or roman letters, is to represent Japanese names on signs, like those in train stations, so that foreigners can read them

EXTENSION ACTIVITY

Have students work in pairs or groups to write five English sentences in kana Then have them trade sentences with their partners or with another group and try to read the sentences.

ANSWERS

1. Konnichi wa; based on the syllabary, students will probably answer konnichi ha.
2. Konban wa; based on the syllabary, students will probably answer konban ha
3. Oyasumi nasai.
4. どうもありがとうございます
5. すみません
6. おげんきですか

ASSESSMENT

Were students able to write simple Japanese sentences in hiragana? Were students able to write their names in hiragana?

Japanese Writing

To read and write in English, you needed to learn 26 characters—the letters of the alphabet Can you imagine learning to read and write with a system that uses almost 2,000 different characters? That's what Japanese students need to do

Japanese uses a system of characters, or *kanji*, based on Chinese writing Each kanji stands for a different word Kanji can also be used in combinations to create new words

Japanese also uses two sets of characters called *kana* Kana stand for sounds in the way our letters do, but most of them stand for a whole syllable, not just a vowel or consonant. Instead of using one symbol for the sound *k* and one for the sound *a*, they use one symbol for the syllable *ka*. Each set of kana has 42 symbols and a few variants

And on top of all that, Japanese students also learn the Western alphabet, which they call *romaji*, or Roman letters

Because of the way Japanese is constructed, all words can be written out in *hiragana*—symbols for Japanese syllables For example, the Japanese for good morning is *ohayo gozaimasu* (oh-hi-oh ge-zigh-e-mass). In hiragana, this would be written

On the following page is a complete set of hiragana. Notice that the addition of two small lines, like quotation marks, changes the consonant sound slightly. The *k* sound becomes *g*, *s* becomes *z*, *t* becomes *d*, and *h* becomes *b*. What mark is used to change the *h* sound to *p*?

_____

(continued)

Japanese Writing (continued)

ひらがな

HIRAGANA

a	あ	i	い	u	う	e	え	o	お
ka	か	ki	き	ku	く	ke	け	ko	こ
sa	さ	shi	し	su	す	se	せ	so	そ
ta	た	chi	ち	tsu	つ	te	て	to	と
na	な	ni	に	nu	ぬ	ne	ね	no	の
ha	は	hi	ひ	fu	ふ	he	へ	ho	ほ
ma	ま	mi	み	mu	む	me	め	mo	も
ya	や			yu	ゆ			yo	よ
ra	ら	ri	り	ru	る	re	れ	ro	ろ
wa	わ							wo	を
n	ん								
ga	が	gi	ぎ	gu	ぐ	ge	げ	go	ご
za	ざ	ji	じ	zu	ず	ze	ぜ	zo	ぞ
da	だ	zi	ぢ	zu	づ	de	で	do	ど
ba	ば	bi	び	bu	ぶ	be	べ	bo	ぼ
pa	ぱ	pi	ぴ	pu	ぷ	pe	ぺ	po	ぽ

(continued)

Japanese Writing (continued)

Practice writing the symbols for the basic vowel sounds.

a あ _____

i い _____

u う _____

e え _____

o お _____

These Japanese phrases have been written in hiragana. Write them in romaji

1. (Good afternoon) こんにちは

2. (Good evening.) こんばんは

3 (Good night) おやすみなさい

These Japanese phrases have been written in romaji. Write them out in hiragana.

4 *Domo arigato gozaimasu* (Thank you very much)

_____

5. *Sumimasen* (Excuse me, pardon me)

_____

6 *Ogenki desu ka?* (How are you?)

_____

Bonus question

Try writing your name in kana Since you can't write consonants out by themselves, you may need to add some vowels into your name. *Mark* might become *Ma-ru-ka*, or *Ma-ru-ko*. Try to get as close as possible to the sound of your name.

_____

Nihon-no-Kotowaza:
Japanese Proverbs

OBJECTIVES

Language Arts

• Students will analyze the meaning of unfamiliar phrases to find parallels with English phrases.

Social Studies

• Students will understand some of the commonalities between different cultures.

MATERIALS

Nihon-no-kotowaza. Japanese Proverbs handout
paper and pencils

BACKGROUND

Nihon is the Japanese word for Japan. *No* is a particle used to express possession. *Kotowaza* means "proverbs." Here are some more examples of Japanese proverbs with English parallels.

Toranu tanuki no kawa zan'you Count the skins of badgers which haven't been caught. English: Don't count your chickens before they're hatched

Neko ni koban. A coin to a cat. English: Pearls before swine.

Sumeba miyako. If residing, capital/metropolis. English: Home is where the heart is.

PROCEDURE

Distribute the handout and discuss it with students. If you want, you can use some of the proverbs given in the Background section as examples while you model the process. Students then proceed as directed on the handout.

ANSWERS

1. Different strokes for different folks.

2. Once a fool, always a fool.

3. Let sleeping dogs lie.

4. If at first you don't succeed, try, try, try again.

5. We all make mistakes sometimes. Or, Pride goes before a fall.

EXTENSION ACTIVITY

If students have done the exercises on Japanese writing and/or counting objects, ask them to try to identify some of the characters in the proverbs. They may recognize the number 10 and the character for people in proverb 1, the numbers 7 and 8 in proverb 4, and kana like *wa, na, kya,* etc.

ASSESSMENT

Were students able to identify similar proverbs in English, or at least to rephrase the Japanese proverbs to sound like English ones?

Nihon-no-Kotowaza: Japanese Proverbs

Proverbs are short sayings that use picturesque language to express a piece of wisdom. All cultures have developed proverbs. Most proverbs reflect the culture they come from. For example, proverbs from the Sahara area may represent water as valuable, and proverbs from Southeast Asia may talk of crocodiles. Often, the same thought is expressed in proverbs from different cultures. For example, Japan has a saying, "Isogaba maware." The literal translation for this is "If hurried, go around." This means that when you're in a hurry it is often faster to take a roundabout route. This is similar to the meaning in the English saying "More haste, less speed."

Here are some more Japanese proverbs with their literal translations. Try to find an English proverb that means something similar to the Japanese one. If you can't find a similar English proverb, rephrase the literal translation so that it sounds like an English proverb.

1. *Juu-nin to-iro.* Ten people, ten colors.

  十人十色

_____

_____

2. *Baka wa shinanakya naoranai.* A fool is only cured by dying.

 馬鹿は死ななきゃ治らない

_____

_____

(continued)

         Hands-on Culture of Japan

Nihon-no-Kotowaza: Japanese Proverbs (continued)

3. *Yabu wo tsutsuite hebi wo dasu.* Poke a bush, a snake comes out.

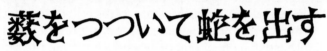

_____

_____

4. *Nana korobi, ya oki.* Seven falls, eight getting up.

_____

_____

5. *Saru mo ki kara ochiru.* Even monkeys fall from trees.

猿も木から落ちる

_____

_____

Glossary

daimyo	feudal lord
fugu	poisonous fish; specially trained chefs remove the poison sacs and serve the fish—usually raw—as a great delicacy
Go	national game of Japan, played on square board with 181 black stones and 180 white ones
gomokunarabe	much simpler game played on Go board
gyotaku	printing method using real fish
haiku	17-syllable poem in 3 lines of 5–7–5 syllables each.
hiragana	Japanese syllabary, often used for verb endings, other grammatical uses
ideogram	picture or symbol used in writing systems
kana	character used to write syllables
kanji	Japanese ideogram writing system, adapted from Chinese system
kappamaki	sushi roll with cucumber
katakana	Japanese syllabary, usually used for foreign words
katazome	Japanese printing technique using stencils and a paste resist
koan	short riddling question asked Zen students as part of their training
mon	family crest or emblem
nori	dried seaweed, used in sushi
Nihon	Japanese name for Japan
samurai	member of the warrior class in feudal Japan
shogun	virtual ruler of Japan up to the Meiji Restoration
sushi	rice seasoned with vinegar, often combined with raw fish or vegetables
washi	handmade Japanese paper
wasabi	very hot green horseradish used with sushi

Resources

General/Art /History

http://www.pem.org/exhibits/mingei/ An exhibit of Japanese arts, including textiles, ceramics, metalwork, wood, and lacquer.

http.//nserv.ei.nsc.co.jp/isei/books/66/isei_66_3 A discussion of various aspects of Japanese culture today.

http.//fuji.sanford.edu/XGUIDE/japan_history_culture_text.html Links to other sites.

Alden, C. Sunrise Island. New York: Parent's Magazine Press, 1971.

DeMente, Boye. *The Whole Japan Book: An Encyclopedia Reader on Things Japanese.* Phoenix: Phoenix Book Publishers, 1983.

Gallery Guide, San Diego Museum of Art. Teaching kit that includes 28 slides of Japanese works. Available from the San Diego Museum of Art, P.O. Box 2107, San Diego, CA 92112-2107.

History of the World's Cultures: Early Japan. New York: Time-Life Books, 1968.

Japan: Images and Words. Available from School and Family Programs, Education Department, Freer/Sackler, MRC 707, Smithsonian Institution, Washington, DC 20560. (202) 357-4880.

Lee, Sherman E. *A History of Far Eastern Art.* Englewood Cliffs, NJ. Prentice-Hall, Inc

Smith, Bradley. *Japan—A History in Art.* New York. Doubleday and Company, Inc., 1964.

Teaching Japan Through the Arts, set of four books: *Natsu Matsuri* (summer festivals), *Traditional Arts and Culture, Japan Through Art Activities,* and *School Days in Japan.* Available from East Asia Resource Center, the University of Washington, Thomson Hall DR05, Seattle, WA 98195. (206) 543-1921.

Zurlo, Tony. *Japan: Superpower of the Pacific.* Dillon Press, 1991. An overview of Japan's history, cultural heritages, and modern society.

Activities

Bernson, Mary Hammond, and Betsy Goolian. *Modern Japan: An Idea Book for K–12 Teachers.* Available from Publications Manager, Social Studies Development Center, Indiana University, 2805 E. 10th Street, Suite 120, Bloomington, IN 47405. (812) 855-3838.

Ekiguchi, Kunio and Ruth S. McCreery. *A Japanese Touch for the Seasons.* Tokyo and New York: Kodansha, 1987.

Japan Activity Sheets. Directions for paper dolls, New Year's cards, chopsticks, paper samurai helmets, cart streamers, and fish printing. Available from The Children's Museum, 300 Congress Street, Boston, MA 02210 (800) 370-5487.

Japanese Prints

http://www.csuohio.edu/history/japan.html: A visual literacy exercise using Japanese prints

Forren, Matthi. *Hokusai, Prints and Drawings* Munich, Germany: Prestel-Verlag, 1991

Hillier, Jack Roland. *The Art of Hokusai in Book Illustration.* Chicago: University of Chicago, 1980.

Ives, Colter F. The Great Wave: *The Influence of Japanese Woodcuts on French Prints* New York: The Metropolitan Museum of Art, 1979.

Sushi

http://inetarmy.hisurf.com/~hinode/history-E.html: A history of sushi

http://www.rain.org/~hutch/sushi.html

Detrick, Mia. *Sushi,* Chronicle Books: San Francisco, 1983.

Green, Karen. *Japanese Cooking for the American Table.* Los Angeles: J.P. Tarcher, Inc., 1982.

Martin, Peter and Joan. *Japanese Cooking.* New York: Gramercy Publishing Company, 1970.

Kinjiro Omae and Yuzuru Tachibana, *The Book of Sushi.* Tokyo: Kodansha International Ltd., 1981.

Rafael Steinberg, *Recipes: The Cooking of Japan.* Food of the World, New York: Time-Life Books,1969.

R. Weston, *Cooking the Japanese Way.* Minneapolis: Lerner Publications, 1983.

Gyotaku

Olander, Doug. *Gyotaku Fish Impressions,* Frank Amato Publications, PO Box 82112, Portland, Oregon, 97282.

Nasco Fish Replicas, 901 Janesville Ave., PO Box 901, Fort Atkinson, WI 53538-0901; 1-800-558-9595.

Counting in Japanese

http://www.bekkoame.or.jp/~yabu/my-hp08.html

Haskins, Jim. *Count Your Way Through Japan.* Illustrated by Martin Skoro. Minneapolis: Carolrhoda Books, 1987.

Paper

http://www.com.rd.pref.gifu.jp/e-main2/kamiwasi/whatwasi.html

Mon

Mizoguchi, Saburo. *Arts of Japan I: Design Motifs.* Weatherhill, New York, 1973.

Japanese Design Motifs: 4,260 Illustrations of Japanese Crests. Compiled by the Matsuya Piece-Goods Store. Translated by Fumie Adachi. New York: Dover Publications, 1972.

Katazome

Nakano, Eisha with Barbara B. Stephan, *Japanese Stencil Dyeing: Paste-resist Techniques*. New York: Weatherhill, 1982.

Haiku

http://www.mlckew.edu.au/departments/japanese/haiku.htm

http://www.obs-us.com/people/sunny/haiku/haikuform.htm

http://www.cs.tufts.edu/~dlipton/haiku.html

http://www.ori.u-tokyo.ac.jp/~dhugal/haikuhome.html

Cohen, William Howard. *To Walk in Seasons*. Rutland, VT and Tokyo, Japan· Charles E. Tuttle Company, 1972.

Higginson, William and Penny Harter. *The Haiku Handbook: How to Write, Share, and Teach Haiku*. Tokyo: Kodansha International, ISBN: 4-7700-1430-0-9.

Issa, Yayu, and Kikaku. *Don't Tell the Scarecrow*. New York: Four Winds Press, 1969.

Japanese Language

http://www.bekkoame.or.jp/~yabu/my-hp16.html

http://www.bekkoame.or.jp/~yabu/my-hp04.html

http://www.bekkoame.or.jp/~yabu/my-hp03.html

http://www.aeonetco.jp/japanese/index.html

http://www.mickey.ai.kyntech.ac.jp/cgi-bin/japanese?CONFIG=&FILE=HTMLFiles

http://www.mickey.ai.kyntech.ac.jp/cgi-bin/japanese?CONFIG=&FILE=HTML-Files/Glossary.html

Japanese Writing Systems

http://www.bekkoame.or.jp/~yabu/my-hp05.html

Zen Gardens

Davidson, A.K. *The Art of Zen Gardens: A Guide to Their Creation and Enjoyment*. Los Angeles: J.P. Tarcher, 1983.

Ohashi, Haruzo. *Japanese Gardens of the Modern Era*. Tokyo, Japan: Graphic-Sha Publishing, 1987.